BIOCHEMICAL SOCIETY SYMPOSIA

No. 25

ASPECTS OF INSECT BIOCHEMISTRY

ASPECTS OF
INSECT BIOCHEMISTRY

Biochemical Society Symposium No. 25
held in London, 1 April, 1965

ORGANIZED AND EDITED BY
T. W. GOODWIN

1965
ACADEMIC PRESS
LONDON and NEW YORK

ACADEMIC PRESS INC. (LONDON) LTD
Berkeley Square House
Berkeley Square
London W.1

U.S. Edition published by

ACADEMIC PRESS INC.
111 Fifth Avenue
New York, New York 10003

Library of Congress Catalog Card Number: 65-27888

PRINTED IN GREAT BRITAIN BY
SPOTTISWOODE BALLANTYNE AND CO. LTD,
LONDON AND COLCHESTER

LIST OF CONTRIBUTORS

P. C. J. Brunet, *Department of Zoology, University of Oxford, England*

T. Bücher, *Physiologisch-Chemisches Institut der Universität München, Germany*

B. A. Kilby, *Department of Biochemistry, University of Leeds, England*

K. M. Rudall, *Astbury Department of Biophysics, The University, Leeds, England*

J. E. Treherne, *A.R.C. Unit of Insect Physiology, Department of Zoology, University of Cambridge, England*

V. B. Wigglesworth, *Department of Zoology, University of Cambridge, England*

F. P. W. Winteringham, *Biochemistry Department, A.R.C. Pest Infestation Laboratory, Slough, England*

PREFACE

THE Biochemical Society is grateful to Professor Sir Vincent Wigglesworth, F.R.S., not only for acting as Chairman for the Symposium but also for agreeing at short notice to give the paper on 'Insect Hormones'. A summary of his lecture is included in this volume, but it was not considered appropriate to provide a full text because this had been done very recently [*A. Rev. Insect Physiol.*, 1964, **2**, 244]; however, a bibliography of recent biochemical work on insect hormones is included.

The organizer would like to thank Dr. P. W. Kent for many useful suggestions during the early stages of arranging this symposium, and the contributors for providing their manuscripts with little procrastination.

T. W. GOODWIN

Department of Biochemistry and Agricultural Biochemistry,
University College of Wales,
Aberystwyth, Cardiganshire, Wales.

CONTENTS

CHAIRMAN'S INTRODUCTION

By V. B. WIGGLESWORTH

THE universality of the basic framework of living matter, whether this be thought of in terms of the fine structure of the cell, or of the chemical processes that go forward within it, is I suppose among the major discoveries of this century. To that I would add the discovery (by the biochemists) that cells do have a structure, and that this structure is really important for their operation—a discovery which has brought biochemistry right back to where it belongs, into the centre of physiology. My revered teacher, Gowland Hopkins, once remarked that 'Life is a dynamic equilibrium in a polyphasic system'. I must confess that I never really liked that way of putting it. As an histologist I should prefer to say that 'Life is a *structure* which controls the chemical processes in its aqueous environment'—that is, in the *milieu intérieur* of the cell.

The virtue of the insects as a medium for the study of physiological chemistry lies in their diversity. Given sufficient acquaintance with them, it is generally possible to find material ideally suited to the study of any problem. They have provided attractive material for the chemistry of natural products, from the purines and pteridines studied by Hopkins in the wing pigments of butterflies, to the aphins described by Todd and his colleagues.

They can be well suited to the study of chemical changes in metabolism. In the early 1920's Otto Warburg had produced evidence for the existence of an enzyme which catalysed the combination of hydrogen with oxygen, the so-called *Atmungsferment*—but the nature of this agent remained undiscovered. In 1925 when David Keilin was studying the haemoglobin that is found in the larva of the horse-bot *Gasterophilus* he rediscovered the absorption bands in insect muscles, which he recognized as bands of a series of haematoporphyrins. Turning to the flight muscles of the bee and of the wax moth, what Keilin saw was entirely new. He saw that these pigments were alternately oxidized and reduced within the living insect. He at once realized that here was the universal oxidizing system that everyone had been looking for: the chain of cytochromes through which electrons were transferred to molecular oxygen so that this became 'activated' and caused to unite with the hydrogen detached from the body fuels. That was a classic piece of insect biochemistry.

There are many specialized and beautiful examples of active transport of water and of ions in specialized organs of insects. Their muscles show structural differences and enzymic specializations which differ enormously from one insect to another or from one part of the body to another. Although the general outlines of metabolism are similar in all animals, there are distinctive characters in certain insects which make them particularly attractive for study.

There are some striking points of resemblance between insects and plants: notably in some of the polymers they produce. I am thinking particularly of that remarkable polymerized protein 'sclerotin', produced through the agency of tanning quinones derived from aromatic amino acids, on the one hand, and of the polysaccharides of the cuticle (the various types of chitin and other mucopolysaccharides) on the other, which remind one respectively of the lignins and of the cellulose of plants.

Finally, the hormones of insects, which have been extensively studied along physiological lines, are beginning to be resolved into known chemical entities, which initiate specific enzyme processes—often, it would appear, by evoking the activity of particular parts of the gene system in the chromosomes.

These are just some of the biochemical topics for the study of which the insect has provided a most suitable medium. And that, I am sure, will be made apparent by the contributions that are to follow.

ACTIVE TRANSPORT IN INSECTS

By J. E. TREHERNE

A.R.C. Unit of Insect Physiology
Department of Zoology, University of Cambridge, England

INTRODUCTION

THE metabolic process of cells and tissues depend upon the maintenance of appropriate concentrations of the various substances involved. In many cases the concentrations of metabolites are maintained at fairly critical levels in the body as a result of energy utilizing processes which are generally described by the term 'active transport'.

This contribution is a brief account of some aspects of the transport processes which have been described in insects. The active transport of non-electrolytes has been little studied in this group of animals and this account will be confined, therefore, to a consideration of the processes involved in the transport of water and inorganic ions. The ability to transport water molecules against osmotic gradients is of obvious selective advantage in such small animals in which the effective conservation of water is a necessity for survival in a terrestrial environment. The presence of mechanisms capable of regulating the levels of inorganic ions in the cells and tissues is also of importance, not only for the adequate functioning of the various excitable systems, but also for the influence which inorganic ions exert on such processes as chromosomal RNA synthesis (Kroeger, 1963) and respiratory metabolism in insects (cf. Harvey, 1965).

WATER

In general the results of investigations on water movements in a variety of cells and tissues from various animal groups have not required the postulation of any specific mechanisms for the transport of this molecule (cf. Andersen & Ussing, 1960; Robinson, 1960). In these studies the apparent movement of water against appreciable osmotic gradients can be explained in terms of factors such as the solute drag observed in electro-osmosis (Diamond, 1962) and in the passive diffusion of ions and molecules (Meschia & Setnikar, 1959; Diamond, 1962) as well as by the co-diffusion resulting from active solute transport (Diamond, 1962). The insects appear to be exceptional in this respect in that a net

1

transport of water against a concentration gradient has been demonstrated in the absence of additional forces such as a hydrostatic pressure gradient or those mentioned above.

The ability of insects to transport water was first demonstrated in a number of experiments which showed that several species were capable of absorbing water through the body surfaces at relative humidities which were well below saturation point (see Beament, 1964, for references). The most remarkable of these insects appears to be the pre-pupa of the flea *Xenopsylla* which is able to extract water from the air at relative humidities as low as 50% (Edney, 1947).

The results of experiments on the uptake of liquid water, applied as droplets to the surface of a cockroach, are also startling (Beament, 1964). The disappearance of droplets of 1·0% NaCl, and also saturated solutions of sodium cyanide and sodium fluoride, was found to occur at approximately similar rates to that of distilled water, leaving solid crystals of these salts on the outside of the animal! The uptake of the water through the superficial cuticular lipid film under these circumstances would have theoretically involved the expenditure of energy sufficient to overcome conventional osmotic forces of the order of 300 atm (Beament, 1964).

Perhaps the most rigorous demonstration of an active secretion of water in insects is that carried out by Phillips (1964b) on the uptake by the rectum of the locust, *Schistocerca gregaria*. This work established that the absorption of water through the rectal wall was quite independent of the movement of other substances and occurred in the absence of a significant hydrostatic pressure gradient. The possibility of any absorption due to electro-osmosis was also eliminated by studies which demonstrated uptake following experimental reversal of the potential difference (15–32 mV) across the gut wall. The rate of absorption of water in these experiments was found to depend upon the osmotic gradient across the rectal wall (Fig. 1). Uptake occurred at about 17 μl/hr in the absence of an osmotic gradient and fell to below zero when it exceeded 0·6 osmoles. The roughly linear relation obtained at concentrations below 0·6 osmoles suggests that the active uptake component (of 17 μl/hr) is superimposed on passive water movements which depend upon the magnitude and direction of the osmotic gradient between the gut lumen and the haemolymph.

An essentially similar active transport of water to that described above has also been demonstrated in the hind-gut of the blowfly, *Calliphora erythrocephala* (Phillips, 1964a). In addition, the possibility exists that an active movement of water may occur through the insect tracheole wall (cf. Beament, 1964). It is significant that all of the well-authenticated cases of an active water movement occur through general integument or through membranes which are derived from infoldings of the integument. Now one of the characteristic features of the arthropod integument is the organized lipid layers which play an important role in restricting water loss to the environment. The presence of such extremely impermeable diffusion barriers would at first sight seem to be an undesirable feature for any actively secreting membrane. Beament (1964) has shown, however, that the absorption of liquid water into the cuticle is probably accompanied by a temporary reorganization of the lipid molecules. This reorganization probably involves a change in the orientation of the polar lipid layer, analogous to that obtained during heating above the transition temperature, when the permeability properties of the lipid film approach that of a perfect semi-permeable membrane.

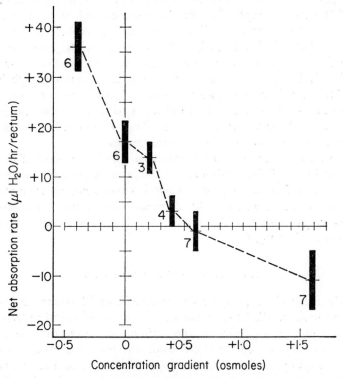

Fig. 1. The relationship between the initial osmotic gradient and the net rate of water movement across the rectal wall of *Schistocerca gregaria* (Phillips, 1964a).

Water uptake can also be imitated in model systems incorporating pieces of dead cuticle, in which the absorptive force is produced by dehydrated proteins (Beament, 1964). Beament has produced a very ingenious model for a cuticular continuous-flow water pump which involves the postulation of cyclical changes in the iso-electric point of the cuticular proteins so as to alter continuously their degree of hydration. Such a water-transporting device requires the presence of a superficial valve mechanism capable of regulating the water movements between the outside medium and the underlying protein layers. The presence of such a valve mechanism may be inferred from the demonstrated asymmetric water permeability of insect cuticle (cf. Beament, 1961). A

2

possible mechanism involving phase changes in cuticular lipids has been proposed which accounts for the variable permeability to water (Locke, 1964). It remains to be seen to what extent this or similar mechanisms can be applied to the other sites of demonstrated transport of water in insects.

INORGANIC IONS

The nature of the mechanisms involved in the transport of inorganic ions in insects is of considerable interest in view of the peculiar composition of the haemolymph of species from orders such as the Lepidoptera, Phasmida, Coleoptera, and Hymenoptera (cf. Wyatt, 1961; Shaw & Stobbart, 1963; Sutcliffe, 1963). The body fluids of species from these orders differ from those of most other animal groups in exhibiting exceedingly low concentrations of sodium and relatively high levels of potassium and magnesium ions. Such specialized environments for the organs of these insects might be expected to be reflected in equivalent specialization in the transport mechanisms involved in the exchanges of inorganic ions between the cells and tissues.

There have been several attempts to define the process of the active transport ions in living systems. For the present purposes an ion will be regarded as being actively transported when a net movement can be shown to occur against an electrochemical gradient and in the absence of significant interactions with the solvent molecules crossing the membrane (Andersen & Ussing, 1960).

Transfer across the cell membrane

The transfer of inorganic ions between cells and the surrounding fluids has been little studied in insects and the only information available is derived from investigations on the ionic regulation of the tissues of the central nervous system. In these studies it has been found possible to separate rapidly exchanging fractions, identified as the extracellular ions, from the more slowly exchanging intracellular ion fractions (Treherne, 1961b, 1962, 1965). The intracellular sodium level of the nerve and tissues was estimated to be lower than that of the extracellular fluid in both *Periplaneta* (Treherne, 1962, 1965) and *Carausius* (Treherne, 1965). In the former species the intracellular concentration was around 67·2 mM/l as compared with a level of 283·6 mM/l in the extracellular, whilst in the latter insect the intracellular medium level was estimated at 86·3 mM/l as compared with the extracellular concentration of 212·4 mM/l. The intracellular potassium levels in the nerve cords of these insects were high, being 225·1 mM/l and 555·8 mM/l respectively, as would be expected from the presence of a Donnan equilibrium with the extracellular fluid (cf. Boyle & Conway, 1941). Now the resting potential for *Periplaneta* giant axons is around 77·0 mV (Narahashi & Yamasaki, 1959), so that with the above concentration ratio for sodium there will be an appreciable electrochemical potential opposing the outward movement of these ions from the axoplasm in this insect.

The low intracellular level of sodium in the nerve cords of these insects is maintained by an outward secretion of this ion, for in the presence of dilute dinitrophenol or cyanide the efflux of radiosodium was found to be significantly reduced (Treherne, 1961a). The effect of dinitrophenol on sodium extrusion represents circumstantial evidence for the involvement of high-energy phosphate compounds in this process, for this inhibitor is known to act by uncoupling oxidative phosphorylation so as to prevent the formation of ATP and to accelerate its hydrolysis (Lipmann, 1941).

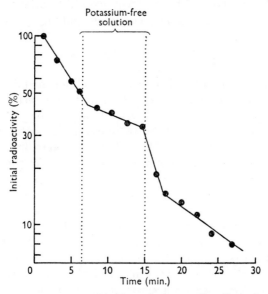

Fig. 2. The effect of potassium-free bathing solution on the efflux of radiosodium from the isolated abdominal nerve cord of the cockroach (Treherne, 1961a).

The small size of the insect axons has, however, prevented any direct experimental demonstration of the involvement of high-energy phosphate compounds in sodium extrusion, by the injection of these compounds into the axoplasm of cyanide-treated axons such as has been carried out with squid giant axons (Caldwell, Hodgkin, Keynes & Shaw, 1960).

The extrusion of intracellular sodium from the nerve cord of *Periplaneta* was found to be unaffected by the replacement of the external sodium with xylose or choline chloride (Treherne, 1961a). The sodium efflux was, however, significantly reduced in the absence of the relatively low concentration of potassium ions (Fig. 2). These observations suggest a coupling of sodium and potassium movements such as has been demonstrated with some other cells (cf. Hodgkin, 1958) and which has led to the hypothesis that the sodium pump may operate by extruding one ion for each potassium ion absorbed (Harris, 1954; Hodgkin &

Keynes, 1954). In the experiments with the nerve cord of *Periplaneta* sodium extrusion in the absence of external potassium did not fall to the same extent as in the presence of metabolic inhibitors (Treherne, 1961a). Such an effect could result from only a partial coupling of sodium efflux and potassium influx, although the possibility cannot be eliminated that it might have resulted from the presence of a residuum of potassium ions in the immediate vicinity of the axon surface in these washed preparations.

The limited amount of information outlined above suggests that the main features of the sodium pump situated in the insect axon membrane are essentially similar to those of the excitable cells from the other animal groups which have so far been investigated.

Transfer across cellular membranes

The movements of inorganic ions across cellular membranes has been studied in a number of insect organs and tissues using a variety of techniques. One of the most convenient organs for the study of the processes involved in the transfer of inorganic ions has been the anal papillae of some aquatic larva. These structures were first demonstrated to be a major site for the osmotic entry of water into the haemolymph (Wigglesworth, 1933) and were later shown to be involved in the uptake of chloride (Koch, 1938; Wigglesworth, 1938; Treherne, 1954b), sodium and potassium ions (Ramsay, 1953a; Treherne, 1954b; Stobbart, 1959, 1960) and phosphate (Hassett & Jenkins, 1951) from dilute solutions. The ventral tube of the collembolan *Produra aquatica* has also been shown to be an important site for the exchange of inorganic ions with the outside medium (Nobel-Nesbitt, 1963). Relatively large fluxes of sodium ions have also been measured through the body wall in *Limnephilus stigmata* (Sutcliffe, 1961).

The movements of several inorganic ions have been extensively studied in investigations on the physiology of Malpighian tubules (Patton & Craig, 1939; Boné & Koch, 1942; Ramsay, 1951, 1952, 1953b, 1955a, b), and the associated absorptive processes in the rectum (Ramsay, 1953a; Shaw, 1955; Sutcliffe, 1961; Phillips, 1964b; Berridge, 1964), while the transfer processes occurring in other regions of the gut have been investigated in larvae of *Aedes aegypti* (Ramsay, 1950) and *Sialis lutaria* (Shaw, 1955) and the larva of *Hylaphora cecropia* (Harvey & Nedergaard, 1964). The movements of inorganic ions across the fibrous and cellular nerve sheath have also been studied in the central nervous systems of *Periplaneta* (Treherne, 1961a, b, 1962) and *Carausius* (Treherne, 1965).

In some of these investigations, sufficient data have been collected to enable conclusive identification of active processes involved in the transport of inorganic ions. The remainder of this section will be concerned with the nature of the mechanisms involved in these processes.

Sodium

There are several examples of apparent active transport of sodium ions across the cellular membranes in insects. This occurs, for example, in the mid-gut of *Sialis lutaria* (Shaw, 1955), the isolated Malpighian tubule of *Carausius morosus* (Ramsay, 1955b), and the rectal wall of *Schistocerca gregaria* (Phillips, 1964b) where movements of this cation occur against electrochemical gradients.

The potential difference across the wall of the anal papillae of *Aedes aegypti* larvae has been found to be as high as -30 mV (Stobbart, 1962). With an external solution of 2·0 mM/l Na the equilibrium concentration in the haemolymph resulting from such a potential difference would be expected to be approximately 6·5 mM/l, as compared with the measured haemolymph concentration of 95–100 mM/l. The solvent drag involved in the osmotic uptake of water by the anal papillae (Wigglesworth, 1933) has been calculated to be a negligible factor in sodium accumulation (Shaw & Stobbart, 1963), so that it can be concluded that an active transport of this cation must occur across the epithelium of these organs. The transport mechanism involved in this ion pump appears to be largely specific for sodium (Treherne, 1954a; Stobbart, 1965).

Our present knowledge of the functioning of the sodium pump in the anal papillae of the mosquito larva is largely derived from measurements of the flux of radiosodium (Treherne, 1954a; Stobbart, 1959, 1960, 1965). Of particular interest are the experiments demonstrating a rapid net uptake of sodium in larvae in which the haemolymph level of this ion was reduced to about one-third of its normal level by rearing the insects in a sodium-deficient medium (Stobbart, 1960). In a medium of 2·0 mM/l the rapid net accumulation of sodium proceeds at a constant rate until the haemolymph level of this ion is achieved. The period of net uptake is accompanied by sodium fluxes which are very many times greater than the steady-state values obtained (Fig. 3). In these experiments sodium efflux was shown to be dependent on the simultaneous influx of the ion. The efflux, therefore, is not merely a consequence of a passive sodium loss and it has been suggested that it includes an exchange component (Stobbart, 1960). The sodium transporting system is thus visualized as consisting of a sodium pump which functions in conjunction with an exchange diffusion mechanism which is postulated to be confined to a sodium-impermeable osmotic barrier in the papillae. According to this model the sodium pump is able to split off at the inner surface of the barrier sufficient sodium to balance passive losses of this ion.

From the few examples available for insects it appears that the movement of sodium ions through complex cellular membranes takes place more rapidly than through the cell membrane. Using the flux measurements of Stobbart (1959) and making a crude estimate of the surface area of the papillae relative to the blood volume of an *Aedes* larva it is possible to calculate a transfer constant (K_{in}) of around $7·60 \times 10^{-4}$ cm sec^{-1} with

an external sodium concentration of 2·0 mM/l. The equivalent transfer
constant for the uptake of sodium into the extracellular fluid of the nerve
cord of *Carausius*, which is assumed to involve some peripheral cellular
layers, can be calculated to be approximately $9·86 \times 10^{-5}$ cm sec^{-1}
(Treherne, 1965). These values can be compared with the transfer
constant (K_{out}) of $1·84 \times 10^{-6}$ cm sec^{-1} for the metabolically maintained
extrusion of sodium across the axon membrane in an isolated cockroach
connective. This value was calculated from the measured half time of
338·0 sec for the intracellular efflux (Treherne, 1961b), assuming a

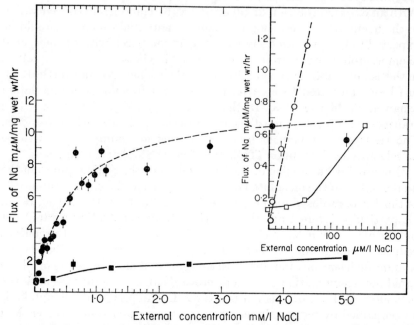

Fig. 3. The relationships between the external sodium concentration and the influx (●)
and efflux (■) of this ion in starved larvae of *Aedes aegypti*. The balance point where
influx = efflux is illustrated in the inset (Stobbart, 1965).

surface volume ratio of approximately 1116·0 cm^{-1} calculated from the
distribution of fibre size given by Roeder (1953) for this preparation.

A recent electron microscope investigation (Copeland, 1964) has
revealed that the cell membrane at the cuticular surface of the epithelium
of the anal papillae of *Aedes* larvae is thrown into deep, narrow, parallel
folds (Fig. 4). This infolding of the outer cell membrane produces more
than a tenfold increase in surface area so that by comparison with the
values quoted above it will be seen that the actual movements of sodium
ions per unit area of surface membrane approaches that across the
plasma membrane of other cells. This extremely large area of cell membrane is also accompanied by the presence of numerous mitochondria and
a plentiful supply of glycogen. The cell surface at the inner surface of the
epithelium is frequently interrupted by the openings of an extensive

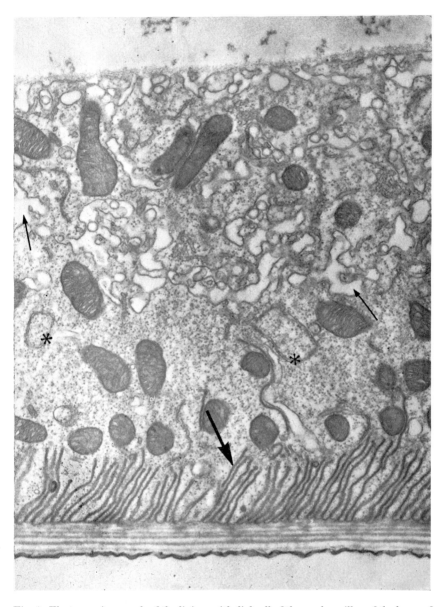

Fig. 4. Electron micrograph of the lining epithelial cell of the anal papillae of the larva of *Aedes aegypti*. The fine parallel folds of the plasma membrane (heavy arrow) adjacent to the cuticle are associated with a plentiful distribution of mitochondria and glycogen deposits. Random elements of the endoplasmic reticulum (asterisks) are seen in association with the basal folds in the form of circular or cup-shaped cisternae. The cell surface at the haemolymph side is interrupted by numerous infoldings or canaliculi (small arrows) which penetrate into the cytoplasm. Approx. × 22,000. (Reproduced by courtesy of Dr. E. Copeland.)

system of canaliculi which results in a large membrane surface at the haemolymph side. The canaliculi are also associated with a plentiful distribution of mitochondria. The association of both the outer and the inner epithelial surfaces with extensive collections of mitochondria suggests that energy expenditure is involved in the transfer of ions across both these membranes. It is tempting to identify the outer surface of the papilla epithelium with the exchange-diffusion mechanism and the inner canalicular surface with the associated ion pump postulated by Stobbart (1959). Now the intracellular sodium level of the few insect tissues which have been investigated appear to be relatively high, averaging 67·2 mM/l and 86·3 mM/l in the nerve cords of *Periplaneta* and *Carausius* (Treherne, 1965), 110·6 mM/l in the muscle fibres of *Periplaneta* (Wood, 1963), and about 55·0 mM/l in the cells of the rectal wall of *Schistocerca* (Phillips, 1964b). By analogy with these examples it is of particular interest to note that the transfer of sodium across the outer epithelial surface would be associated with a steep concentration gradient, relative to the dilute level in the outside medium. It follows from this that any pumping of sodium across the inner surface of the epithelial cells would involve the transfer against a much less steep concentration gradient, for the sodium level of *Aedes* haemolymph is in the region of 95–100 mM/l (Ramsay, 1953a; Stobbart, 1959).

Finally it is of some interest to mention the observation of a specific inhibition of net sodium transport in the larva of *Chironomus* which occurs in the presence of anticholinesterases (Koch, 1954). As in *Aedes* larvae, the anal papillae of *Chironomus* are concerned with ionic uptake (Koch, 1938), so that it is surprising to find that in the former species sodium transport is not affected by eserine (Stobbart, 1960). This difference might suggest that some differences exist between the sodium transporting mechanisms in the organs of quite closely related species.

Potassium

Insect tissues are unusual in possessing the ability actively to transport potassium ions. The existence of a potassium pump in a cellular membrane was first demonstrated in Malpighian tubules, where accumulation of this cation was found to occur against an appreciable electrochemical gradient (Ramsay, 1953b). Solvent drag does not appear to be an important factor in the transport of potassium across the tubule wall (Shaw & Stobbart, 1963). The concentration of potassium in tubule fluid appears to be related to the level of the ion in the haemolymph, for the tubular concentration of potassium in *Carausius*, showed a progressive increase until a level of about 50·0 mM/l was reached in the haemolymph (Ramsay, 1955b). Potassium movement in the isolated tubule can also be related to the rate of fluid production and it has been suggested that the active transport of this ion is the prime mover in generating the flow of urine into the tubule lumen (Ramsay, 1953b, 1954, 1955b, 1956).

A potassium pump has recently been identified in the midgut of the larva of *Hylaphora cecropia* (Harvey & Nedergaard, 1964). The presence of such a mechanism in this region of the gut can be correlated with the diet of this phytophagous larva. The potassium content of a typical food plant of this species, *Viburnum notatum*, averaged 153 mM as compared with the sodium level of 4 mM. The potassium/sodium ratio in the midgut is even more extreme, averaging 208 mM potassium to 0·7 mM sodium (Harvey & Nedergaard, 1964).

In the fifth instar of *Hylaphora* there is an average potential of 84 mV across the midgut wall, the lumen being positive with respect to the haemolymph (Harvey & Nedergaard, 1964). When this potential is

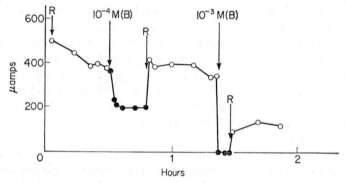

Fig. 5. The effect of sodium sulphide, at two concentrations, on the short-circuit current across the midgut wall of the larva of *Hylaphora cecropia* (Haskell, Clemons and Harvey, 1965).

short circuited there is an average current of 614 μAmps across the gut wall. Flux measurements with ^{42}K indicate that the greater part of this current is maintained by the active transport of potassium into the midgut lumen. Of particular interest is the observation that sodium does not appear to be involved in this potassium transport, for essentially similar potential differences, short circuit currents and potassium fluxes were obtained in the absence of this cation. This potassium transport thus appears to be fundamentally different from that across the membrane in one insect cell type in which potassium efflux has been shown to be linked to sodium movements (Treherne, 1961a). The inhibitors of normal sodium-potassium-linked transport including ouabain, were also without effect on potassium movements across the midgut wall (Haskell, Clemons & Harvey, 1965). Treatment with dinitrophenol, iodoacetic acid, carbon dioxide and oxygen lack, all resulted in a reduction of the short circuit current, indicating that this potassium pump probably depends upon phosphorylation and glycolytic pathways in the energy-trapping mechanism.

The inhibition of current at moderately alkaline pH, together with the inhibitory effects of carbon dioxide and the carbonic anhydrase inhibitors, cardrase and sodium sulphide (Fig. 5) suggest that potassium transport may be linked to the movement of hydrogen ions in the midgut of this insect.

Chloride

The uptake of chloride ions against steep concentration gradients was first demonstrated in the anal papillae of Culicine larvae (Koch, 1938; Wigglesworth, 1938) and was later shown to occur in the equivalent organs of the larvae of the beetles *Helodes minuta* and *H. marginata* (Treherne, 1954b). The uptake of chloride by the anal papillae of *Aedes* larvae involves an accumulation against an electrochemical gradient (Stobbart, 1965) indicating the presence of an active transport mechanism for this anion.

In these experiments the potential between the haemolymph and the outside solution of potassium chloride became negative after about half an hour, suggesting that under some circumstances active chloride transport may exceed that of the cation (Stobbart, 1965). A chloride-transporting mechanism which is separate from that responsible for the uptake of sodium has also been postulated in the rectal chamber of the larvae of *Libellula* and *Aeschna* (Krogh, 1939). An uptake of chloride ions against electrochemical gradients has also been demonstrated across the rectal wall in *Sialis* larvae (Shaw, 1955) and in *Schistocerca* (Phillips, 1964b).

CONCLUSIONS

This brief account has served to show that insects exhibit several unusual features in the processes involved in the active transport of water and inorganic ions. In particular the insects and some related groups of arthropods may be unique in their ability to transport water against osmotic gradients by mechanisms which are independent of the movement of other substances and which function in the absence of significant hydrostatic pressure gradients. It seems likely that this ability may have developed as a result of the specialized organization of the integument in this group of animals.

The transport of monovalent cations across the cell membrane, in one instance at least, is effected by a sodium-potassium linked system which is essentially similar to those which have been demonstrated in the membranes of cells from other animal groups. Transport across the complex cellular membrane of the Cecropia midgut on the other hand, shows that the transport of potassium is achieved by a sodium-independent mechanism which also shows marked differences with respect to the metabolic inhibitors known to affect the conventional linked sodium-potassium pump. Differences may also exist in the functioning of the sodium pump situated in the same organ in quite closely related groups. This is illustrated by the differences in sensitivity of the sodium transporting mechanism in the anal papillae of larvae of *Aedes* and *Chironomus* to anticholinesterases.

These examples serve to emphasize that there is likely to be a diversity of transport mechanisms in insect cells and tissues and that even sodium and potassium transport cannot be accounted for by a single mechanism.

REFERENCES

Andersen, B. & Ussing, H. H. (1960). In *Comparative Biochemistry*. Eds. M. Florkin and M. H. Mason. London: Academic Press.

Beament, J. W. L. (1961). *Biol. Rev.* **36**, 281.

Beament, J. W. L. (1964). *Adv. Insect Physiol.* **2**, 67.

Berridge, M. J. (1964). Ph.D. Thesis, University of Cambridge.

Boné, G. & Koch, H. J. (1942). *Ann. Soc. Zool. Belg.* **73**, 73.

Boyle, P. J. & Conway, E. J. (1941). *J. Physiol.* **100**, 1.

Caldwell, P. C., Hodgkin, A. L., Keynes, R. D. & Shaw, T. I. (1960). *J. Physiol.* **152**, 561.

Copeland, E. (1964). *J. Cell Biol.* **23**, 253.

Diamond, J. (1962). *J. Physiol.* **161**, 503.

Edney, E. B. (1947). *Bull. Ent. Res.* **38**, 263.

Harris, E. J. (1954). *Symp. Soc. exp. Biol.* 8, 228.

Harvey, W. R. (1965). *Adv. Insect Physiol.* **3** (in Press).

Harvey, W. R. & Nedergaard, S. (1964). *Proc. nat. Acad. Sci.* **51**, 757.

Haskell, J. A., Clemons, R. D. & Harvey, W. R. (1965). *J. cell. comp. Physiol.* **65**, 45.

Hassett, C. C. & Jenkins, D. W. (1951). *Physiol. Zool.* **24**, 257.

Hodgkin, A. L. (1958). *Proc. R. Soc.* B **148**, 1.

Hodgkin, A. L. & Keynes, R. D. (1954). *Symp. Soc. exp. Biol.* 8, 423.

Koch, H. (1938). *J. exp. Biol.* **15**, 152.

Koch, H. (1954). *Arch. Int. Physiol.* **62**, 136.

Kroeger, H. (1963). *Nature, Lond.* **200**, 1234.

Krogh, A. (1939). *Osmotic Regulation in Aquatic Animals*. Cambridge University Press.

Lipmann, F. (1941). *Adv. Enzymol.* **1**, 99.

Locke, M. (1965). *Science* 147, 295.

Meschia, G. & Setnikar, L. (1959). *J. gen. Physiol.* **42**, 429.

Narahashi, T. & Yamasaki, T. (1959). *J. Insect Physiol.* **3**, 146.

Nobel-Nesbitt, J. J. (1963). *J. exp. Biol.* **40**, 701.

Patton, R. L. & Craig, R. (1939). *J. exp. Zool.* **81**, 437.

Phillips, J. E. (1964a). *J. exp. Biol.* **41**, 15.

Phillips, J. E. (1964b). *J. exp. Biol.* **41**, 39.

Ramsay, J. A. (1950). *J. exp. Biol.* **27**, 145.

Ramsay, J. A. (1951). *J. exp. Biol.* **28**, 62.

Ramsay, J. A. (1952). *J. exp. Biol.* **29**, 110.

Ramsay, J. A. (1953a). *J. exp. Biol.* **30**, 79.

Ramsay, J. A. (1953b). *J. exp. Biol.* **30**, 358.

Ramsay, J. A. (1954). *J. exp. Biol.* **31**, 104.

Ramsay, J. A. (1955a). *J. exp. Biol.* **32**, 183.

Ramsay, J. A. (1955b). *J. exp. Biol.* **32**, 200.

Ramsay J. A. (1956). *J. exp. Biol.* **33**, 697.

Robinson, J. R. (1960). *Physiol. Rev.* **40**, 112.

Roeder, K. D. (1953). In *Insect Physiology*. Ed. K. D. Roeder. New York: Wiley.

Shaw, J. (1955). *J. exp. Biol.* **32**, 330.

Shaw, J. & Stobbart, R. H. (1963). *Adv. Insect Physiol.* **1**, 315.

Stobbart, R. H. (1959). *J. exp. Biol.* **36**, 641.

Stobbart, R. H. (1960). *J. exp. Biol.* **37**, 549.

Stobbart, R. H. (1962). Quoted in Shaw & Stobbart (1963).

Stobbart, R. H. (1965). *J. exp. Biol.* **42**, 29.

Sutcliffe, D. W. (1961). *J. exp. Biol.* **38**, 521.

Sutcliffe, D. W. (1963). *Comp. Biochem. Physiol.* **9**, 121.
Treherne, J. E. (1954a). *J. exp. Biol.* **31**, 386.
Treherne, J. E. (1954b). *Trans. R. Ent. Soc., Lond.* **105**, 117.
Treherne, J. E. (1961a). *J. exp. Biol.* **38**, 629.
Treherne, J. E. (1961b). *J. exp. Biol.* **38**, 737.
Treherne, J. E. (1962). *J. exp. Biol.* **39**, 193.
Treherne, J. E. (1965). *J. exp. Biol.* **42**, 7.
Wigglesworth, V. B. (1933). *J. exp. Biol.* **10**, 1.
Wigglesworth, V. B. (1938). *J. exp. Biol.* **15**, 235.
Wood, D. W. (1963). *Comp. Biochem. Physiol.* **9**, 151.
Wyatt, G. R. (1961). *A. Rev. Ent.* **6**, 75.

DISCUSSION

D. F. Evered*: Dr. Treherne has already carried out some experiments upon amino acid transport in the desert locust. He will already be aware that potassium ions and amino acids show a reciprocal relationship in uptake studies with many mammalian systems. Do insect systems also show this fundamental characteristic?

J. E. Treherne: My own work on amino acid absorption from the midgut showed that the net absorption of glycine and serine depended upon the diffusion gradient created by the relatively rapid removal of water into the haemolymph. There is at the moment, in fact, no evidence of active transport of amino acids from the insect gut. There has been no work carried out in insects on the interactions of potassium and amino acid movements.

* Department of Chemistry, Chelsea College of Science and Technology, London, England.

FORMATION OF THE SPECIFIC STRUCTURAL AND ENZYMIC PATTERN OF THE INSECT FLIGHT MUSCLE

By TH. BÜCHER

Physiologisch-Chemisches Institut der Universität München, Germany

INSECT muscles are particularly appropriate objects for studying morphogenetic processes. In a symposium with Sir Vincent Wigglesworth as chairman there is no need for further explanation of this fact. He demonstrated in his pioneer investigations that the muscular system develops in stages. There is already a predetermination in the egg. Hormones are responsible for the single morphogenetic processes.

Owing to the rapid succession of generations the insect organism has a relatively old phylogenetic age. Accordingly it is highly developed. This can be concluded not only from the morphological but also from the physiological structure of all functional units. From the technical point of view this high degree of specialization is of advantage. The tissues are of restricted complexity. For that reason we find models for different distinct morphological processes among the insects.

From this aspect, taking the flight muscle as an example, I wish to discuss in some detail the formation of four structures. In Fig. 1 they can be recognized in a longitudinal section of the adult flight muscle.

1. The mitochondria (M), which are responsible for the extreme respiratory rate of the organ during activity (Watanabe & Williams, 1951, 1954; Sacktor, 1959; Bücher, Klingenberg & Zebe, 1959).

2. The interfibrillar tracheoles (Tr) which wind round the mitochondrial columns providing them with oxygen (Edwards & Ruska, 1955).

3. The specific enzymic pattern of carbohydrate disintegration which provides the mitochondria with substrate. Their localization is extra-mitochondrial, predominantly in the region of the Z-zones (Vogell, Bishai, Bücher, Klingenberg, Pette & Zebe, 1959; Siess & Pette, 1960).

4. The myofibrils which transform the potential of chemical reactivity into work.

We have obtained the African locust, *Locusta migratoria*, the subject for our investigations, and instructions for their breeding from London (Hunter-Jones, 1961). I want to use this opportunity to express my warmest thanks to Mr. Philip Hunter-Jones and his co-workers for their kind help for many years.

The flight muscle of *Locusta migratoria* is a particularly useful tissue. During the past few years the status of the adult muscle of this insect has been characterized extensively by both morphological and biochemical investigations. Weis-Fogh has examined the metabolism of this organ during rest and activity (Krogh & Weis-Fogh, 1951; Weis-Fogh, 1952), and from the work of Klingenberg and his colleagues we understand the structure, function, dynamics and compartmentation of the mito-chondria of this muscle as well as or even better than the classical objects of investigation of the chondriologists (Klingenberg & Bücher, 1959, 1961; Klingenberg, 1964; Klingenberg & Bode, 1965).

The teams of Vogell and of Pette have been working at the localization of the enzymes in this organ (Pette, Vogell & Brandau, 1962; Pette & Brandau, 1962). Last but not least, this tissue has served to develop basic quantitative views on the order of enzyme activity patterns (Delbrück, Zebe & Bücher, 1959; Vogell *et al.*, 1959; Bücher, 1960; Bücher & Pette, 1961; Pette & Bücher, 1965).

PRECURSOR

The development of this muscle, highly specialized in function and structure, begins after the fourth moult, as was shown by my colleague Bishai several years ago (Bishai, Vogell & Bücher, 1960; Bishai, 1960). It develops from an 'Anlage' which is situated at the same region in the thorax. In a longitudinal section in Fig. 2 this 'Anlage' can also be recognized as a muscle. We have called it 'precursor muscle'. The precursor muscle is only slightly differentiated. It is rich in nuclei (Nm). The localization of the chromatin at the periphery indicates a high activity of the nucleus which is also reflected by the richness of the cytoplasm in polysomes (R). Vogell (1962) has identified the polysomes histochemically by application of ribonuclease. They are the reason for the basophilia which was seen earlier by Wigglesworth during the trans-formation of the muscles of the bug. The precursor muscle already contains fully functioning but very small mitochondria (M) which will enter a phase of rapid growth. However, interfibrillar tracheoles cannot be found. Also some of the characteristic properties of the enzymic pattern of the adult flight muscle are still absent.

By reference to Fig. 3 an interesting aspect of the enzymic pattern can be discussed. This aspect may contribute to the question whether our precursor muscle is an ordinary skeletal muscle or not.

AEROBIC AND ANAEROBIC METABOLISM

As discovered by Brosemer (Brosemer, Vogell & Bücher, 1963) the precursor muscle shows very little lactate dehydrogenase (LDH) activity,

Fig. 1. *Locusta migratoria*. Adult flight muscle 8 days after imaginal moult. Longitudinal section (× **13,000**).

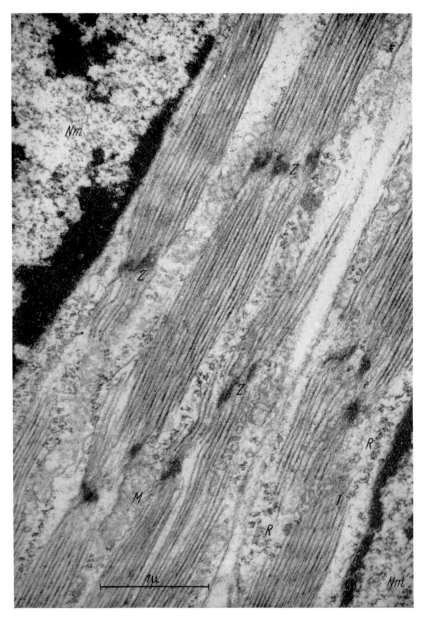

Fig. 2. Precursor muscle on the 1st day after fourth moult. Longitudinal section
(× 30,000).

either absolutely or compared with the other glycolytic enzymes. At this point the specific enzymic pattern of the adult muscle is already pre-formed, a fact interesting from several points of view.

1. This absence of enzyme is by no means due to a general lack of information on the genome of the locust. Ordinary skeletal muscles, for

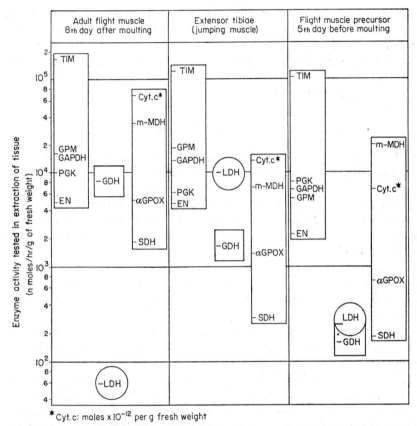

Fig. 3. Enzyme activity pattern of the adult flight muscle, of the adult jumping muscle and of the flight muscle precursor 5 days before imaginal moult. Key to Figs. 3 and 6: CE = Condensing enzyme; Cyt. c = cytochrome c; EN = enolase; GAPDH = glyceraldehyde 3-phosphate dehydrogenase; GDH = α-glycerophosphate dehydrogenase (NAD specific); GPM = glycerate 3-phosphate mutase; αGPOX = glycerol 1-phosphate oxidase; IDH = isocitrate dehydrogenase (TPN specific); LDH = lactate dehydrogenase; MDH = malate dehydrogenase; PGK = glycerate 3-phosphate kinase; SDH = succinate dehydrogenase; TIM = triose phosphate isomerase.

instance the jumping muscle in the hind leg of the insect (Fig. 3), have a high level of lactate dehydrogenase (Zebe & McShan, 1957; Zebe, Delbrück & Bücher, 1957, 1959; Vogell et al., 1959). The jumping muscle, like the precursor of the flight muscle, is poor in mitochondria. Its enzymic pattern, however, reflects a considerable ability for anaerobic activity comparable to skeletal muscles of warm-blooded animals. Its ability to form lactic acid is high and is needed during the jump. There are also muscles of this kind with high lactate dehydrogenase activity in the thorax, those muscles which move the forelegs, the head and so on. In contrast a characteristic of insect flight muscles is that oxygen is provided by interfibrillar tracheoles winding round mitochondrial columns; furthermore capacity for lactic acid formation is almost completely absent. This specific feature is characteristic for all flying insects, no matter whether flight depends exclusively on carbohydrate (Diptera), exclusively on fat (Lepidoptera) or is of the mixed carbohydrate-fat type (as in *Locusta*).

2. Absence of lactate dehydrogenase in the precursor muscle means that the intensive development during the formation of the flight muscle is essentially an aerobic process.

PHASES DURING FORMATION OF THE FLIGHT MUSCLE

The mass of the dorsal-longitudinal precursor muscle after the end of the fourth moult is about 4 mg fresh weight (Brosemer *et al.*, 1963; Beenakkers, 1963). During the following 2 weeks it increases by a factor of about 12 (Fig. 4). As to the weight, four phases of the developmental process can be distinguished: larval growth, moulting interval, phase of differentiation and phase of duplication. This subdivision is confirmed when morphological and chemical parameters are compared.

During the first larval phase all cellular components increase on a logarithmic scale—except the number of nuclei which remains constant. The increase of the cellular components is rather unspecific and without marked differentiation.

During the second phase, directly before and after the imaginal moult, the increase of weight stops. As a result of the collapse in oxygen supply energy is probably lacking. It is during this second phase that the system of tracheas and tracheoles is reconstructed. In particular, tracheoles are now invaginated into the flight muscle. This will be discussed later.

During the third phase there is new growth, but now with complete differentiation of the morphological and enzymological pattern at the same time. Therefore we have called this phase 'the phase of differentiation'. At the end of this phase the animals begin to flutter their wings but are not yet able to fly. Eventually, starting at the 5th day, all components of the flight muscle are duplicated. This duplication is not seen very clearly in the figure, which represents only the fresh weight. It is, however, a very interesting phenomenon which will also be discussed later. But now, first, we must consider what happens to the single components.

MITOCHONDRIA

The chondriome makes up about 6% of the volume of the precursor muscle (Fig. 5). In the adult muscle the chondriome makes up 30% of the volume. At the same time the total muscle volume increases by a factor

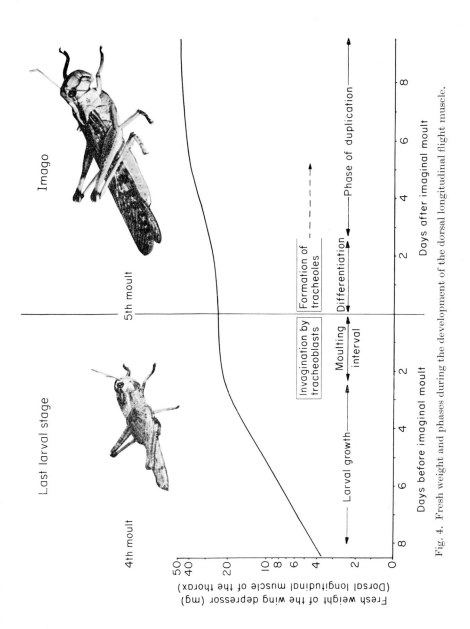

Fig. 4. Fresh weight and phases during the development of the dorsal longitudinal flight muscle.

of 10. Thus the increase of the chondriome is about fiftyfold. As demonstrated in Fig. 5, this increase is mainly caused by growth of the mitochondria. Electron microscopy also reveals divisions of mitochondria (see Brosemer *et al.*, 1963).

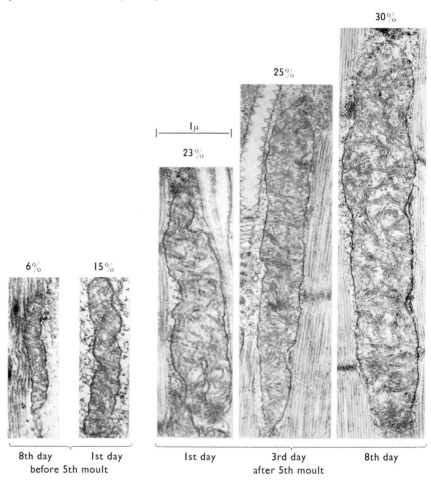

Fig. 5. The shape of mitochondria and volume fraction (%) during the development of the flight muscle.

This increase of the chondriome can be recognized as well by quantitative analysis of the electron microscope pictures as well as by measurement of mitochondrial enzymic activities (Table 1). The relation between the increase of mitochondrial structures, evaluated by Dr. Vogell according to Buffon's needle method, and the increase of mitochondrial enzymes is very close. As a representative enzyme in this table mitochondrial glycerol-1-phosphate oxidase, the enzyme of Meyerhof and Green, which is fixed to the mitochondrial membranes, is used. The quotient of increase in membrane profile and enzymic activity is constant within the experimental error of the analyses. This parallelism between increase in morphological mitochondrial structure and the enzyme content does not leave any doubt about the independent growth of mitochondrial structure. Simultaneously with our investigations this fact was also observed in quite a different way by Luck (1963) with *Neurospora*.

Table 1. *Histiometric and enzymic analysis of mitochondrial growth*

Mitochondrial parameter	Days before imaginal moulting				After imaginal moulting		
	8th	5th	2nd	1st	2 hr	3 days	8 days
a = volume fraction	6%	8%	15%	15%	23%	25%	30%
b = membrane profile $[\mu/\mu^2]$	50	40	40	40	30	45	56
(a)×(b)	300	320	600	600	690	1130	1680
Activity of αGPOX $[\mu\text{moles/hr/gf}]$	—	700	1100	1125	1350	2260	3290
$\dfrac{\alpha\text{GPOX}}{(\text{a})\times(\text{b})}$	—	2·2	1·8	1·9	1·9	2·0	2·0

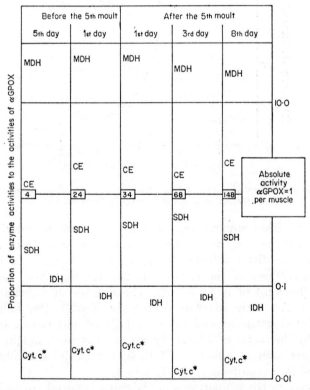

Fig. 6. Pattern of mitochondrial enzyme activities during development of the flight muscle. The abbreviations used in the diagram are explained in legend to Fig. 3 (p. 17).

4

So far we have only demonstrated the enzymic activity of glycerol 1-phosphate oxidase. Brosemer *et al.* (1963) and Beenakkers (1963) extended this comparison to a dozen different mitochondrial enzymes, some fixed to the structure and non-extractable, some easily extractable. They showed a constant enzyme pattern in the precursor muscle and in the adult muscle. This means that growth of the mitochondria is synchronous in all elements. In Fig. 6 the mitochondrial enzymic activities are plotted relative to that of the glycerol 1-phosphate oxidase which served as a reference. The increase in mitochondrial mass is reflected by

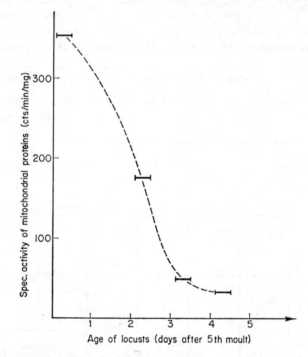

Fig. 8. Rate of incorporation of [^{14}C]isoleucine *in vitro* into mitochondria isolated a different stages of the developing flight muscle.

the figures within squares representing the absolute activity of the reference enzyme per dorsal longitudinal thorax muscle. Chondriogenesis is most distinct during the phase of duplication. In Fig. 7 one sees cross sections of the muscle, at the 4th day (top) and on the 8th day (bottom) of imaginal life. The number of myofilaments per myofibril is 210 on the left, 430 on the right. Equally the profiles of the mitochondrial cristae as well as the activity of mitochondrial enzymes increase by the factor of 2 (activity per gram of fresh weight and total fresh weight each by a factor of 1·4). As can easily be recognized, the mitochondrial envelope is perfectly intact.

Constancy in the proportions of the mitochondrial enzymic pattern during the development of muscles has, incidentally, not been observed

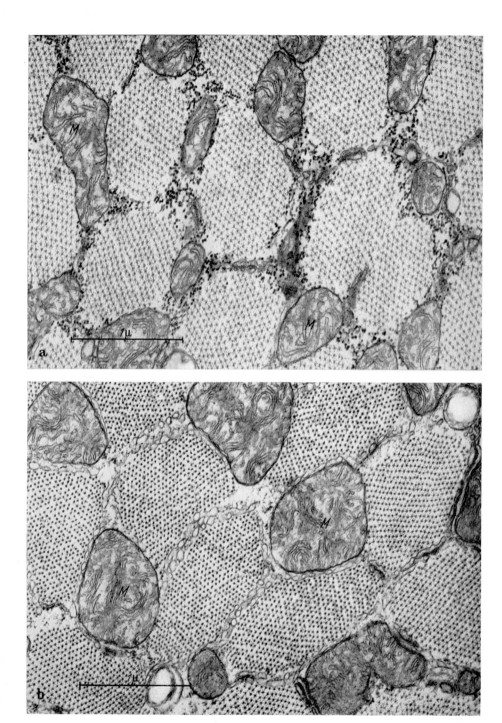

Fig. 7. Cross section (× 30,000) of the dorsal longitudinal muscle at the beginning and at the end of the duplication phase. a: 4th day, b: 8th day after imaginal moult.

to the same extent by Michejda (1963) with silkworm, or by Herold (1961) with the honeybee. One can say, however, that the old hypothesis of Williams regarding the control of the development by the formation of cytochrome *c*, has been disproved by all later investigations. On the

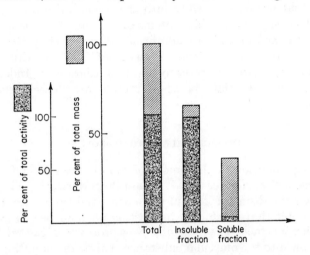

Fig. 9. Mass and activity of the mitochondrial fractions after incubation with [^{14}C]iso-leucine for 1 hr *in vitro*.

contrary, one would be tempted to conclude that the mitochondria are functionally active at all stages and that mitochondrial growth is induced by metabolic requirements. This idea too, however, must at least be

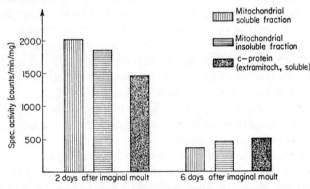

Fig. 10. Specific activity of flight muscle proteins 24 hr after the injection of 0·3 μC [^{14}C]isoleucine per animal.

modified from investigations *in vitro*. As Neupert & Bücher (1964) and Bronsert & Schott (1964) showed recently the process of the formation of flight muscle mitochondria can be observed *in vitro* by measuring the incorporation of labelled amino acids. Interestingly the incorporation rate into *isolated* mitochondria *in vitro* is dependent on the stage of development of the muscle from which those mitochondria have been isolated. This is shown in Fig. 8. Analogous to the findings of Roodyn (1962) with liver mitochondria, the amino acids are incorporated *in vitro* into flight muscle mitochondria only into the non-extractable part of the mitochondrial protein—possibly into the structural protein (Fig. 9)—whereas the easily extractable proteins of the mitochondria are labelled only when the amino acids are administered *in vivo* (Fig. 10).

According to these results growth of mitochondria depends on co-operation with extra mitochondrial ribosomes. Indeed, mitochondria in the essential phases of growth are densely surrounded by polysomes.

INTERFIBRILLAR TRACHEOLES

As already mentioned, the precursor muscle does not possess interfibrillar tracheoles. Neither does it obtain them during larval growth. It is only after the disintegration of the extrastitial tracheoles during the imaginal moult that the highly interesting phenomenon of intrastitial invagination by tracheoblasts begins. Now processes of the tracheoblasts quickly grow into the muscular substance. This is the moulting interval, when growth of the muscle itself stops.

The invaginating processes (Fig. 11) of the tracheoblasts (Trb) are coated with two double membranes, the sarcolemma (SL) of the muscular fibre and the plasmalemma (PL) of the tracheoblasts (Edwards, Ruska & De Harven, 1958; Smith, 1961). The invading tracheoblasts are rich in protoplasm and contain an extended Golgi apparatus but almost no mitochondria. Only after the imaginal moult (Fig. 12) do tracheoles form inside the tracheoblasts. After this the sheath of protoplasm disappears. There now remains the functioning, that is easily permeable, tracheole.

The invagination of the tracheoblasts is a process of more general interest (Wigglesworth, 1959a). It demonstrates the phenomenon of infiltrating penetration of two cellular units, the muscle and the tracheoblasts. We have to consider the mechanism involved.

1. The embryologist would say that a high mutual affinity develops on the surfaces of both cellular units. The molecular mechanism of such an affinity has yet to be investigated.

2. The metabolic basis of the process is interesting too. As a result of the collapse of the tracheal system during the moult oxygen is lacking. Moreover, there are no or almost no mitochondria. In contrast we find an increase in the activity of lactate dehydrogenase in the enzymic pattern. Its maximum occurs in the moult interval (Fig. 13), so there is every reason to believe, on the basis of glycolysis, that invagination of the tracheoblasts—in contrast to the growth of the muscular substance—is anaerobic. This process then would have a certain similarity to the infiltrating growth of malignant tumours which also shows high aerobic glycolysis.

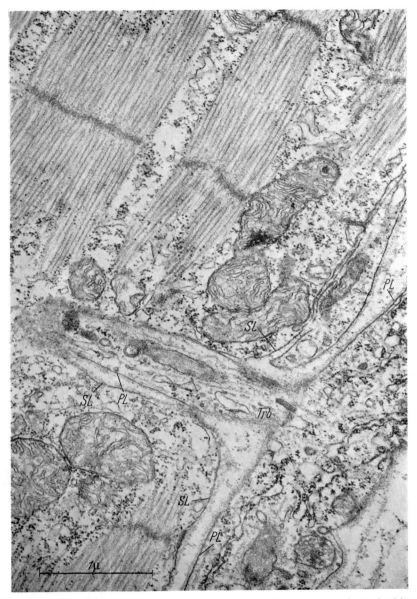

Fig. 11. Moulting interval on the day before imaginal moulting. Invasion of a tracheoblast process (× 30,000).

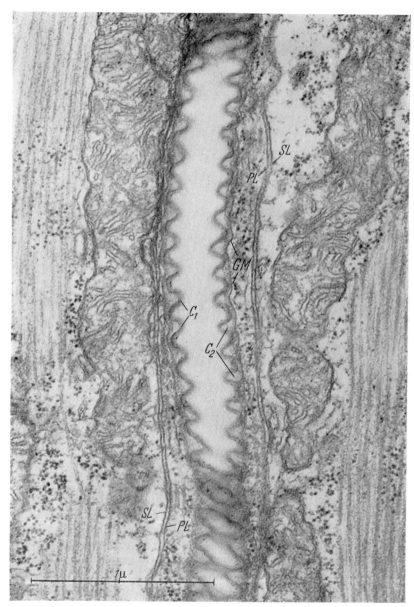

Fig. 12. Formation of an interfibrillar tracheole 2 hr after imaginal moult. The tracheolar intima consists of chitinous exocuticule (C_1) and of 'basement membrane-like' endocuticule (C_2). It is separated from the surrounding cytoplasm by a limiting membrane (GM). The process itself is surrounded by the plasmalemma (PL) of the tracheal end cell and by the sarcolemma (SL) of the muscle cell ($\times 50,000$).

ENZYMES OF THE EMBDEN–MEYERHOF PATHWAY

We now have to consider the development of the pattern of extramito-chondrial enzymes. It may seem to be illogical to discuss it now since carbohydrate break-down (glycolysis) occurs before oxygen consumption and before mitochondrial electron transport. But as just demonstrated we have to deal in our subject with the development of two tissues of different metabolic character. Consequently we can only analyse the enzymic patterns on the basis of the morphologic processes.

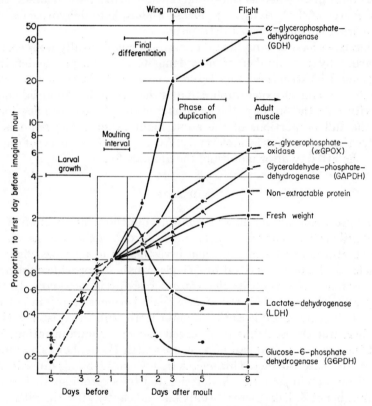

Fig. 13. Phases of development of the biochemical pattern.

In Fig. 13 the changes in representative biochemical parameters are shown. They are: fresh weight, which we discussed earlier (p. 18), non-extractable protein made up partly by mitochondrial fractions but chiefly by the contractile proteins, the glycerol 1-phosphate oxidase (α-GPOX) representing the constant proportion complement of mito-chondrial enzymes (see Fig. 6) and, finally, four enzymes of the extra-mitochondrial carbohydrate breakdown: glyceraldehyde 3-phosphate dehydrogenase (GAPDH), glycerol 1-phosphate dehydrogenase (GDH), lactate dehydrogenase (LDH) and glucose 6-phosphate dehydrogenase (G6PDH); GAPDH is representative of the constant proportion quintet of glycolytic enzymes (Fig. 3). During the first phase of larval growth the exponential increase of all parameters is almost equal. The growth constant is about 0·4 per day.

During the moulting interval the increase in all components, except lactate dehydrogenase, stops. The increase in lactate dehydrogenase shows a peak which can possibly be attributed to the growth of the tracheoblasts. We have discussed this previously.

Next, the enzymologically most interesting phase of differentiation follows. The activity of glycerol 1-phosphate dehydrogenase increases by a factor of 20 whereas that of lactate dehydrogenase again decreases by a factor of 3. Activities of glucose 6-phosphate dehydrogenase and some other enzymes almost disappear.

Finally we have the duplication phase. Morphologically we recognized it earlier by the number of myofilaments and the profile-density of mitochondrial structures (see Table 1 and Fig. 7). At the same time we also find an almost exact duplication of the extramitochondrial enzyme activities. At the 3rd day, the beginning of the phase of duplication, we see the full proportions of the adult flight muscle. The animals now flutter their wings but cannot yet fly. At the end of the phase of duplication, the 8th day after moulting, the animals fly.

MYOFIBRILS

The precursor muscle shows myofibrils, but the cross-striation of these myofibrils is irregular (Fig. 2). This may be one of the reasons why this muscle appears to be empty when investigated in polarized light, like muscles of the bug described by Wigglesworth. To provide evidence for the existence of myofibrils electron microscopy is necessary. Immediately after the last moult the muscle again becomes empty in polarized light. This is remarkable as the myofibrils are still in register with one another. But Dr. K. Allmann observed (personal communication, 1965) that the cross-striation can now be seen with Heidenhain's staining as well as in phasecontrast. This means that A- and I-bands differ in mass, but their protein structure is deteriorated by stretching. Incidentally, the number of Z-disks increases only insignificantly after the fifth moult. Thus, there are two reasons for the polarization optical behaviour during muscle development: (1) transversal order of the sarcomeres, and (2) state of the proteins within the sarcomeres. The latter disorder possibly is connected with the completion of the contractile protein.

An interesting phenomenon is the numerical order of the myofilaments. In the beginning their numbers differ. At the end of the larval phase two groups of myofibrils can be distinguished (Fig. 14), one of round profile with about 65 myofilaments, the other of oblong profile with about 310 myofilaments. The variation in either group is ± 20%. After moulting these differences disappear. At the beginning of the phase of duplication we find 210 (± 10%) myofilaments per myofibril; at the end of the phase of duplication 430 (± 5%) myofilaments. The number of myofibrils

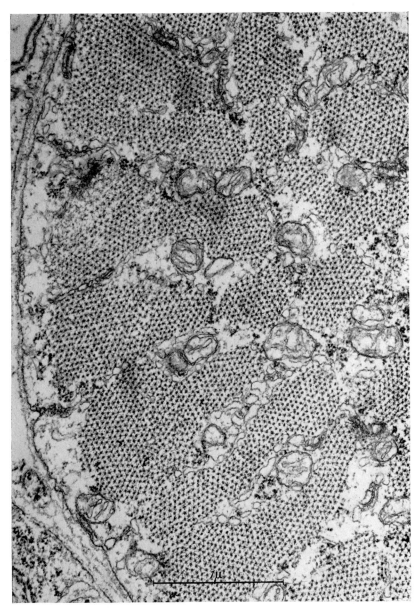

Fig. 14. Larval growth phase on the 3rd day after fourth moulting. Cross section showing the round profiled and oblong profiled myofibrils mentioned in the text (× 35,000).

increases from about 30 per muscle fibre to about 1000. So the contractile system during growth approaches a state of order from several directions. (1) The Z-disks increase numerically and arrange into register. This happens during the larval phase, together with the completion of Z-disk formation. (2) During the last phase the myofibrils reach a remarkably constant number of myofilaments.

The principles by which this geometric order in either dimension is controlled has yet to be investigated.

FINAL REMARKS

In this survey I have concentrated on describing phenomena rather than on discussing mechanisms. As has been suggested earlier, the development of the flight muscle can be compared with the development of a photographic plate. The plate has already been exposed before we begin our investigations. The developing of the latent picture occurs in stages and is induced by specific agents as the hormone 'ecdysone' and is influenced by characteristic features of the whole organism, such as the possibilities for supply of oxygen and substrate.

These interrelations have ingeniously been concluded in earlier years from mainly morphological findings (e.g. Williams, 1953; Wigglesworth, 1959a). By observing biochemical parameters we get a more comprehensive knowledge. For instance, we recognize the predetermination of physiological structure by the drastic reduction of lactate dehydrogenase activity already in the precursor muscle, or by the specific proportions of the enzyme complement of its mitochondria. On the other hand, during the phase of differentiation we still find parameters increasing by an order of magnitude, e.g. the increase of glycerol 1-phosphate dehydrogenase (GDH, Fig. 13) by a factor of 20.

The process of fusion of two cellular units, of the tracheoblast system and of the muscular syncytium is another morphogenetic event. It has been investigated in detail for the first time during the course of our investigations.

These investigations have been supported by the Deutsche Forschungsgemeinschaft (Schwerpunktprogramm Experimentelle Zellforschung). Mr. Uwe Krieg has been kind enough to translate the manuscript.

REFERENCES

Beenakkers, A. M. Th. (1963). *Biochem. Z.* **337**, 436.
Bishai, F. R. (1960). Dissertation, Philosophische Fakultät der Ain Shams Universität, Cairo, Abbasia.
Bishai, F. R., Vogell, W. & Bücher, Th. (1960). *Europ. Symp. med. Enzymol.*, Mailand, S. 13.
Bronsert, U. & Schott, H. (1964). Herbsttagung der Gesellschaft für Physiologische Chemie, Köln.
Brosemer, R. W., Vogell, W. & Bücher, Th. (1963). *Biochem. Z.* **338**, 854.

Bücher, Th. (1960). *Boll. Soc. ital. Biol. sper.* **36**, 1509.

Bücher, Th., Klingenberg, M. & Zebe, E. (1959). *Proc. IVth int. Congr. Biochem.* Vienna 1958, Symp. XII, p. 153, London.

Bücher, Th. & Pette, D. (1961). *Proc. Vth int. Congr. Biochem.* Moscow, III, 271. New York: Pergamon Press and Macmillan.

Delbrück, A., Zebe, E. & Bücher, Th. (1959). *Biochem. Z.* **331**. 273.

Edwards, G. A. & Ruska, H. (1955). *Q. Jl. microsc. Sci.* **96**, 151.

Edwards, G. A., Ruska, H. & De Harven, E. (1958). *Arch. Biol.* (*Liège*) **69**, 351.

Herold, R. C. (1961). Thesis, Science Faculty, University of Pennsylvania.

Hunter-Jones, P. (1961). Rearing and Breeding Locusts in the Laboratory Anti-Locust Research Centre, Wright's Lane, London, W.8.

Klingenberg, M. (1964). *Ergebn. d. Physiologie, Biologischen Chemie u. Exp. Pharmakologie*, **55**, 131.

Klingenberg, M. & Bode, Chr. (1965). *Biochem. Z.* **341**, 271–299.

Klingenberg, M. & Bücher, Th. (1959). *Biochem. Z.* **331**, 312.

Klingenberg, M. & Bücher, Th. (1961). *Biochem. Z.* **334**, 1.

Krogh, A. & Weis-Fogh, T. (1951). *J. exp. Biol.* **28**, 344.

Luck, D. J. L. (1963). *J. Cell Biol.* **16**, 483.

Michejda, J. (1963). *Bull. Soc. des Amis des Sciences et des Lettres de Poznàn*, Serie D, IV, 61.

Neupert, W. & Bücher, Th. (1964). *Herbsttagung der Ges. f. Physiol. Chemie*, Köln.

Pette, D. (1965). *Naturwissenschaften* (in press).

Pette, D., Vogell, W. & Brandau, H. (1962). *Vth Internat. Congr. Electron. Micr.* Philadelphia.

Pette, D. & Brandau, H. (1962). *Biochem. biophys. Res. Commun.* **9**, 367.

Roodyn, D. B. (1962). *Biochem. J.* **85**, 177.

Sacktor, B. (1959). *Proc. IVth int. Congr. Biochem.* Vienna, Symp. XII, p. 138 ff. London.

Siess, M. & Pette, D. (1960). *Biochem. Z.* **332**, 495.

Smith, D. S. (1961). *J. biophys. biochem. Cytol.* **10**, Suppl; 123.

Vogell, W. (1962). *S. B. Ges. Beförd. ges. Naturwiss.* Marburg 83/84, 297.

Vogell, W., Bishai, F. R., Bücher, Th., Klingenberg, M., Pette, D. & Zebe, E. (1959). *Biochem. Z.* **332**, 81.

Watanabe, M. J. & Williams, C. M. (1951). *J. gen. Physiol.* **34**, 675.

Watanabe, M. J. & Williams, C. M. (1954). *J. gen. Physiol.* **37**, 71.

Weis-Fogh, T. (1952). *Phil. Trans.* (B) **237**, 1.

Wigglesworth, V. B. (1959a). *The Control of Growth and Form.* Ithaca, New York, Cornell University Press.

Wigglesworth, V. B. (1959b). *J. exp. Biol.* **36**, 632.

Williams, C. M. (1953). *Harvey Lect.* **47**, 126.

Zebe, E. & McShan, W. H. (1957). *J. gen. Physiol.* **40**, 779.

Zebe, E., Delbrück, A. & Bücher, Th. (1957). *Ber. ges. Physiol.* **189**, 115; *Angew. Chem.* **69**, 65.

Zebe, E., Delbrück, A. & Bücher, Th. (1959). *Biochem. Z.* **331**, 254.

SOME DISTINCTIVE FEATURES OF
INSECT METABOLISM

By F. P. W. WINTERINGHAM

Biochemistry Department,
Agricultural Research Council Pest Infestation Laboratory,
Slough, Buckinghamshire, England

THERE are obvious morphological and behavioural differences between insect and other animal classes. These imply corresponding differences at the molecular level. Their study is not only of interest to the comparative biochemist but is of importance in the development of safer and more selective chemicals for controlling insect pests and vectors of disease. This contribution is an attempt briefly to summarize these differences with some reference to their possible exploitation in the development of safer and more selective insecticides.

It is an unfortunate fact that some of the biochemical differences between insects and vertebrates tend to render insects less vulnerable to toxic compounds. Thus, dicoumarol rapidly induces hypothrombinemia in many vertebrate species and its effect may be reversed by vitamin K. This vitamin plays an important role in the hepatic formation of prothrombin in mammals (Green, 1963). Chemical relatives of dicoumarol such as 3-(α-acetonylbenzyl)-4-hydroxycoumarin (Warfarin) are used commercially for rodent control and their action on ingestion by mammals is characterized by decreased prothrombin levels, defects in blood clotting and internal haemorrhage. Insects appear to have no dietary requirement for vitamin K (Levinson, 1955) and have no vascular blood system so that the anticoagulant mechanism of coumarol and its chemical relatives would not be expected to be of significance in insects. Warfarin baits, for example, can apparently be attacked and consumed by cockroaches with impunity and the related 2-isovaleryl-1-3-indandione (Valone) is of low oral toxicity to the cockroach, *Periplaneta americana* (see Negherbon, 1959, p. 425). However, while there are some reasons for believing that insects would be less susceptible to antivitamin K action certain compounds of this group such as Pival and Valone are insecticidal apparently for other reasons. Pival is toxic to both higher animals and to the housefly, *Musca domestica*, the former showing symptoms of antivitamin K action and haemorrhagic manifestations which could be reversed by the administration of vitamin K. Valone is similarly toxic but the antivitamin K effects in mammals are

29

less pronounced. Vitamin K antagonists can uncouple oxidative phosphorylation in both mammals and insects (Novotny & Kubista, 1960). Martius (1961) has ascribed a role to vitamin K in oxidative phosphorylation. If, on the other hand, vitamin K is not a dietary essential because it is not significant in insect metabolism, then the uncoupling action of these compounds in insects and mammals might not involve vitamin K despite Martius's hypothesis, which has indeed been challenged by other workers (see Pitt & Morton, 1962). It is perhaps significant that vitamin K had little effect on Valone poisoning in rats. These observations suggest that compounds of this class may induce two biochemical lesions, haemorrhagic lesions as a result of their antivitamin K action and an uncoupling or inhibitory action not involving vitamin K, the former being more important in mammals while the latter is more important in insects.

Fraenkel and his colleagues demonstrated many years ago that some insect species (Tenebrionid beetles) require a dietary source of carnitine (Fraenkel, 1951). The wide distribution of this substance in the animal kingdom suggests that these insects lack one or more of the steps of its normal biosynthesis.

Recent and current studies of insect phospholipids by Newburgh and his colleagues in Oregon, Hodgson and his colleagues in Raleigh and by the author's colleagues Bridges and Crone at Slough, have indicated some apparently special features of insect lipid metabolism. Choline is a dietary essential for the normal growth and development of several insect species and of other animals. It is used for the synthesis of lecithins and acetylcholine, the latter playing a vital role in certain nervous synaptic transmission processes. These workers have shown that in Dipterous insects (houseflies and blowflies) dietary choline may be replaced by carnitine, β-methylcholine, γ-butyrobetaine, etc. When the choline is replaced in the larval diet by carnitine, γ-butyrobetaine or by β-methylcholine, the phospholipids containing choline are almost completely replaced by phospholipids containing β-methylcholine. Phospholipids occur in high proportions in cell membranes, mitochondria and insect flight muscle sarcosomes and are believed to play an important role in transport processes. Current studies by Bridges (personal communication) suggest that although the base moiety of the phospholipid may be replaced in this way there was not a parallel replacement of the choline of the central nervous tissue. Thus, to quote Bridges, it seems that 'The β-methylcholine displaces the small amount of choline available to the insect from non-essential sites making it available for essential sites such as the nervous system'. Crone & Bridges (1963) made the interesting observation that while the ^{14}C of labelled serine was incorporated into the cephalins there was a lack of incorporation into the lecithins. This suggests that methylation of phosphatidylethanolamine to phosphatidylcholine, as is known to be possible in mammalian tissues, may not occur in some insects. Diptera appear to be the only group of animals able to spare their choline requirement with carnitine.

Dietary tryptophan cannot spare the nicotinic acid requirement of at least three insect species (of *Drosophila, Phormia* and *Tenebrio*) as it can in some vertebrates and microorganisms where nicotinic acid can be derived biosynthetically from tryptophan. The formation of the insect ommochrome pigments via 3-hydroxykynurenine appears to replace the later steps of nicotinic acid biosynthesis (Henderson, Gholson & Dalgliesh, 1962) of vertebrates. In vertebrates a pyridoxine-deficient diet leads to the accumulation and excretion of 3-hydroxykynurenine. The nicotinic acid requirement of some insect species, despite the occurrence of 3-hydroxykynurenine or 3-hydroxyanthranilic acid suggests that one or more of the later steps to nicotinic acid are missing. Thanks to the elegant work of Butenandt (1959) and his colleagues, it is known that tryptophan and hydroxykynurenine are precursors of the characteristic insect ommochrome pigments. The steps leading to the formation of these pigments then appear to be an alternative pathway of hydroxykynurenine metabolism to that leading to nicotinic acid in some other animals.

It is now well established that insects require a dietary source of cholesterol or of a related sterol for their normal growth and metamorphosis (Clayton, 1964). Like other arthropods they lack the biosynthetic ability of mammals to make sterols from C-2 units. Carnivorous insect species such as *Dermestes vulpinis* are restricted to the so-called zoosterols like cholesterol while phytophagous insects may utilize either zoosterols or phytosterols such as ergosterol. Phytophagous insects thus appear able to conduct limited modifications of the ingested sterol. Early investigations had shown that neither mevalonic acid, squalene, lanosterol nor zymosterol was able to relieve the sterol deficiency syndrome of insects. Casida and his colleagues (Agarwal, Casida & Beck, 1961) concluded that the principal sterol throughout the life of the adult housefly was not cholesterol but a close relative which they designated *muscasterol*. Later, Thomson and his colleagues (1963), using houseflies reared on the same diet, showed that *muscasterol* was campesterol, a homologue of cholesterol. Some β-sitosterol was also present and both sterols occurred in the diet used. Similarly the 24-methylene sterol found in the honeybee *Apis mellifera* is also present in the dietary pollen (Duperon, Hugel, Sipal & Barbier, 1964). There have been occasional reports that insect sterols become labelled following the administration of [^{14}C]acetate, but it is now believed that such synthesis, if it occurred, was due to symbiotic or other microflora (see Clayton, 1964). Saito and his colleagues (1963) have reported that while the synthesis of [^{14}C]sterol from administered [2-^{14}C]acetate was insignificant in the silkworm larva there was significant incorporation at the pre-pupal and non-diapausing pupal stages. This raises the important question of whether the biosynthesis of sterol from C-2 units might take place only at certain stages of the insect's life cycle. Little is known of the possible structural or metabolic roles of insect sterols but recent investigations have indicated that cholesterol is a precursor of the insect prothoracic gland hormone, ecdysone (Karlson & Hoffmeister, 1963). Thus substances interfering with sterol utilization might have a profound effect on the development of insects. Noland (1954) reported that such compounds as cholesteryl chloride, cholesteryl methyl ether and thiocholesteryl acetate inhibited the growth of *Blattella germanica* by competitive inhibition of cholesterol utilization, but this has been challenged by Robbins and his colleagues (1961). Despite their steroid structures the *Veratrum* or *Solanum* alkaloids did not owe their insecticidal action against developing housefly larvae to cholesterol antagonism (Bergmann, Levinson & Mechoulam, 1958).

In some insect species, but perhaps not in all, the disaccharide trehalose plays a similar role to the glucose of vertebrate blood (see p. 42; Wyatt & Kalf, 1957). Candy & Kilby (1961) studied the biosynthesis of trehalose in the locust fat body which appears to be the principal site of biosynthesis. The reactions involve uridine diphosphate intermediates. The biosynthesis of trehalose by insect fat body therefore resembles that in yeast. Treherne (1958) studied the absorption of glucose across the gut wall of the locust and reported that absorption was a process of facilitated diffusion, the necessary concentration gradients being maintained by the conversion of blood glucose into trehalose. The absorption of glucose in this way therefore differs from the active transport mechanisms believed to obtain in vertebrates. In some insect species the fall in the level of haemolymph trehalose during muscular activity or starvation has suggested its role as an immediately available carbohydrate reserve (Clegg & Evans, 1961; Evans & Dethier, 1957; Saito, 1960). Hansen (1964) was unable to find free trehalose in the blood of two species of locusts and has implied that the early reports of insect trehalose may have been the result of inadequate identification of the disaccharide. Hansen detected maltose and cellobiose, the former having also been reported in the crab *Hemigrapsa nudus*.

The flight muscle of some insects is characterized by high glycerol 1-phosphate dehydrogenase/lactic acid dehydrogenase ratios which have important implications for electron transport during flight (see p. 17). Under anaerobic conditions this has the consequence that glycerol 1-phosphate and pyruvate accumulate instead of the lactic acid found in vertebrate and other insect muscle (Kubista, 1957; Winteringham, 1960). Although alanine also accumulated in intact adult houseflies under conditions of anoxia (Price, 1963), there was evidence that glycolytically formed pyruvate was not the sole precursor of the accumulated alanine.

Some insect tissues may accumulate high concentrations of glycerol or sorbitol glycolytically during diapause and these apparently play a role in protection against cold (Chino, 1958, 1961; Salt, 1957, 1958, 1961). The concurrent glycolysis and implied maintenance of ATP levels and the protection of the tissues against freezing by the diversion of glycolytic intermediates to the formation of alcohols suggests a beautiful economy in the resting insect. Baldwin & Needham (1934) reported the presence of phosphoarginine in the thoracic tissues of adult blowflies and this was in agreement with the earlier reports that phosphoarginine was the phosphagen of invertebrate species instead of the phosphocreatine of vertebrates. Winteringham and his colleagues (1955) later reported the presence of phosphoarginine in the thoracic tissues of the adult housefly. Sacktor (1961) has queried the role of phosphoarginine in insects on the grounds of his own failure to demonstrate phosphorylation of arginine by insect tissues *in vitro* in the presence of ATP, etc. However, my colleagues Lewis & Fowler (1962) successfully demonstrated a phospho-arginine kinase *in vitro* using thoracic tissues of the adult blowfly. There is thus strong evidence that phosphoarginine is the phosphagen of insect flight muscle.

Insect tissues contain relatively high concentrations of free amino acids, especially glutamate and proline, which become depleted under conditions of stimulated respiration (e.g. during flight, insecticidal convulsions, etc.) with an increase in glutamine or alanine under the same conditions. Several observations point to the utilization of proline, especially under conditions of insecticidally stimulated respiration or flight (Corrigan & Kearns, 1963; Bursell, 1963). These observations suggest that proline and other amino acids indirectly or directly exchange-able with the keto-acid intermediates of carbohydrate metabolism provide a source of oxidizable substrate, the amino nitrogen appearing as glutamine or alanine during this process as indicated by Winteringham (1958) on the basis of his own observations. Chadwick (1947) noted the lack of free ammonia during the flight of *Drosophila*, which would be consistent with the appearance of amino nitrogen as glutamine or other non-volatile amine. In this same context it is interesting to note that Ray (1964) observed a fall in the concentrations of free proline in the central nerve cord of the cockroach *Periplaneta americana* poisoned with con-vulsant insecticides and the concentration of free glutamine rose. This suggests that stimulated activity of the nerve may also result in the utilization of free amino acids present in nervous tissues. Van den Bergh (1964) has recently criticized the suggestion of amino acids providing an energy source on the grounds that added amino acids were not readily oxidized by housefly sarcosome preparations *in vitro* except by trans-amination of aspartate with pyruvate so that the oxidation of 1 mol of glutamate or proline could only be at the expense of 1 mol of pyruvate which could be converted to alanine. However, *in vivo* there is evidence that the end product may not only be alanine but glutamine so that 1 mol of proline could be oxidized completely by 1 mol of glutamate and not pyruvate.

There is evidence of significant differences between the biochemistry of insect and vertebrate peripheral nervous tissue. The insect myoneural junction is insensitive to curare but that of some lepidopterous species is highly and specifically sensitive to the venoms of certain parasitic wasps, the latter being without effect in mammals (Beard, 1952; Waller, 1964). Peripheral nerve is relatively insensitive to cholinergic blocking agents (Harlow, 1958). Other amines have been implicated as possible neural transmitter substances in addition to the acetylcholine of the central nervous system. There have been various reports in the literature of the presence of adrenaline or adrenaline-like substances in insect tissues (Ostlund, 1954) but neither their presence nor their function in nervous tissue has been confirmed unequivocally. Frontali (1964) and her colleagues have reported the presence of γ-aminobutyric acid in the brain tissue of at least two species of insects together with the presence of glutamic acid decarboxylase but their possible roles in insect central nerve function are unknown. Davey (1961a, b, 1962, 1963) and Hodgson & Geldiay (1959) have reported the release of a cockroach heart accelerating factor in the corpora cardiaca under conditions of artificially stimulated hyperactivity. This factor behaves as a peptide or protein which acts by causing the release of an amine by the pericardial cells. The amine was apparently not adrenaline. Many years ago Roeder and his colleagues demonstrated the great sensitivity of the cockroach heart to the accelerating effects of 5-hydroxytryptamine. Davey (1960) has also reported a secretion of the opaque accessory glands of male insects which also accelerated the cockroach heart, was destroyed by amine oxidase and had properties resembling an o-dihydroxyindolealkylamine. If these substances differ from those associated with central and peripheral nervous function in vertebrates, then a study of their chemistry and enzymic regulation is likely to prove to be a particularly fruitful area in the development of selective insecticides since the nervous tissues of insects are certainly relatively accessible to externally applied lipophilic nerve poisons.

The spectacular processes of moulting and metamorphosis are associated with distinctive metabolic pathways and mechanisms of hormonal regulation. In this context insects produce biosynthetically many specialized products such as silk and chitin. These processes clearly involve products, intermediates, enzymes and hormones which are unlikely to be of significance in vertebrate biochemistry. Thus, Sekeris (1964) has reported that N-acetyldopamine is the sclerotizing agent in the blowfly Calliphora and that the biosynthetic pathway is controlled by ecdysone which induces the synthesis of a key enzyme dihydroxyphenylalanine decarboxylase (Karlson & Sekeris, 1962). As already mentioned, ecdysone appears to be a unique steroid of which dietary cholesterol seems likely to be the precursor.

Interest has recently become focused upon farnesol and its derivatives such as the o-methyl farnesyl ether which has the properties of the insect juvenile hormone (Schmialek, 1961; Wigglesworth, 1963).* The isoprene

* Since presenting this review an important paper on this subject by Meyer, Schneiderman & Gilbert (1965) has appeared which casts considerable doubt on the identity of farnesol or its derivatives with the juvenile hormone of insects.

unit which occurs in farnesol also occurs in certain pheromone-like substances such as the dendrolasin secreted by Formicine ants and this suggests a common biosynthetic pathway for isoprene synthesis. The physiological role of the so-called juvenile hormone is discussed later (p. 80); here it is sufficient to say that according to the concentration and possibly according to the distribution of the hormone the ecdysone-stimulated syntheses are effectively directed towards further larval, pupal or adult tissues and organs. Clements and his colleagues of the Milstead Laboratory at Sittingbourne are currently studying the biosynthesis of open chain isoprenoid compounds such as farnesol from likely precursors such as mevalonic acid. Their preliminary results (Clements & Popják, 1965) indicate that in the adult silk moth *Samia cynthia* [2-^{14}C]mevalonic acid is a precursor of an open chain polyisoprenoid compound.

Foreign compounds including insecticides tend to be metabolized by insects as in other animals but there are significant qualitative and quantitative differences. In mammals, phenols are conjugated as glucosiduronides while in insects they appear as β-glucosides. This appears to be a qualitative difference in enzymic detoxication (Smith, 1955). The detoxication of foreign compounds by insects and mammals has recently been reviewed by Winteringham (1965). Metabolism involving enzymic dehydrohalogenations, amine or phosphorothioate oxidation, phosphatase, and carboxyesterase action are common to both insects and mammals. Enzymic oxidation can be demonstrated with microsomal preparations from insects and mammals and all these processes tend to be inhibited by the so-called methylene dioxyphenol synergists. There are some important quantitative differences in the metabolism of insecticides by insects and mammals. Thus, the favourable mammalian/insect toxicity ratio of the insecticide malathion is due to the greater carboxyesterase activity of the mammalian tissue. Dipterous insects resistant to DDT may have much higher concentrations of DDT-dehydrochlorinase than susceptible ones. This area holds particular promise in the rational development of more selective insecticides.

In conclusion, there are some significant biochemical differences between insects and other animal classes. While it might be claimed that their study has already influenced the rational search for safer and more selective insecticides their calculated exploitation remains in the future.

REFERENCES

Agarwal, H. C., Casida, J. E. & Beck, S. D. (1961). *J. Insect Physiol.* **7**, 32–35.
Baldwin, E. & Needham, D. M. (1934). *J. Physiol.* **80**, 221–237.
Beard, R. L. (1952). *Bull. Conn. agric. Exp. Stn* No. 562.
Bergh, S. G. van den (1964). *Biochem. J.* **93**, 128–136.
Bergmann, E. D., Levinson, Z. H. & Mechoulam, R. (1958).*J. Insect Physiol.* **2**, 162–177.
Bursell, E. (1963). *J. Insect Physiol.* **9**, 439–452.
Butenandt, A. (1959). *Naturwissenschaften* **15**, 461–471.

Candy, D. J. & Kilby, B. A. (1961). *Biochem. J.* **78**, 531–536.

Chadwick, L. E. (1947). *Biol. Bull. mar. biol. Lab., Woods Hole* **93**, 229–239.

Chino, H. (1958). *J. Insect Physiol.* **2**, 1–12.

Chino, H. (1961). *J. Insect Physiol.* **6**, 231.

Clayton, R. B. (1964). *J. Lipid Res.* **5**, 3–19.

Clegg, J. S. & Evans, D. R. (1961). *Science* **234**, 54–55.

Clements, A. N. & Popják, G. J. (1965). *Contr. XIIth Int. Congr. Ent., London.*

Corrigan, J. J. & Kearns, C. W. (1963). *J. Insect Physiol.* **9**, 1–12.

Crone, H. D. & Bridges, R. G. (1963). *Biochem. J.* **89**, 11–21.

Davey, K. G. (1960). *Can. J. Zool.* **38**, 39–45.

Davey, K. G. (1961a). *Gen. comp. Endocr.* **1**, 24–29.

Davey, K. G. (1961b). *Nature, Lond.* **192**, 284.

Davey, K. G. (1962). *Q. Jl. microsc. Sci.* **103**, 349–358.

Davey, K. G. (1963). *J. Insect Physiol.* **9**, 375–381.

Duperon, P., Hugel, M. F., Sipal, Z. & Barbier, M. (1964). *Comp. Biochem. Physiol.* **11**, 257–262.

Evans, D. R. & Dethier, V. G. (1957). *J. Insect Physiol.* **1**, 3–17.

Fraenkel, G. S. (1951). *Arch. Biochem. Biophys.* **34**, 468–477.

Frontali, N. (1964). *Proc. Vth Int. Neurochem. Symp., Austria*, 1962.

Green, J. (1963). In *Metabolic Inhibitors*. Ed. R. H. Hochster and J. H. Quastel, Vol. 1, 407–443. New York and London: Academic Press.

Hansen, O. (1964). *Biochem. J.* **92**, 333–337.

Harlow, P. A. (1958). *Ann. appl. Biol.* **46**, 55–73.

Henderson, L. M., Gholson, R. K. & Dalgliesh, C. E. (1962). In *Comparative Biochemistry. A Comprehensive Treatise.* Vol. 4, Part B, pp. 245–342. New York and London: Academic Press.

Hodgson, E. S. & Geldiay, S. (1959). *Biol. Bull. mar. biol. Lab., Woods Hole* **117**, 275–283.

Karlson, P. & Hoffmeister, H. (1963). *Hoppe-Seyler's Z. physiol. Chem.* **331**, 298–300.

Karlson, P. & Sekeris, C. E. (1962). *Nature, Lond.* **195**, 183–184.

Kubista, V. (1957). *Nature, Lond.* **180**, 549.

Levinson, Z. H. (1955). *Riv. Parasst.* **16**, 1–48.

Lewis, S. E. & Fowler, K. S. (1962). *Nature, Lond.* **194**, 1178–1179.

Martius, C. (1961). *CIBA Foundation Symp. Quinones in electron transport*, 312–326.

Meyer, A. S., Schneiderman, H. A., & Gilbert, L. I. (1965). *Nature, Lond.* **206**, 272–275.

Negherbon, W. O. (1959). *Handbook of Toxicology, III: Insecticides. A compendium.* W. B. Saunders & Co., Philadelphia and London.

Noland, J. L. (1954). *Arch. Biochem. Biophys.* **52**, 323–336.

Novotny, I. & Kubista, V. (1960). *Experientia* **16**, 457.

Östlund, E. (1954). *Acta physiol. scand.* **31**, 1–67.

Pitt, G. A. J. & Morton, R. A. (1962). *A. Rev. Biochem.* **31**, 491–514.

Price, G. M. (1963). *Biochem. J.* **86**, 372–378.

Ray, J. W. (1964). *J. Insect Physiol.* **10**, 587–597.

Robbins, W. E., Kaplanis, J. N., Monroe, K. E. & Tabor, L. A. (1961). *Ann. ent. Soc. Am.* **54**, 165–168.

Sacktor, B. (1961). *A. Rev. Ent.* **6**, 103–130.

Saito, M., Yamazaki, M. & Kobayashi, M. (1963). *Nature, Lond.* **198**, 1324.

Saito, S. (1960). *J. Biochem., Tokyo* **48**, 101–109.

Salt, R. W. (1957). *Can. Ent.* **89**, 491–494.

Salt, R. W. (1958). *Nature, Lond.* **181**, 1281.

Salt, R. W. (1961). *A. Rev. Ent.* **6**, 55–74.

Schmialek, P. (1961). *Z. Naturf.* **16b**, 461–463.

Sekeris, C. E. (1964). *Science* **144**, 419–421.

Smith, J. N. (1955). *Biochem. J.* **60**, 436–442.

Thompson, M. J., Louloudes, S. J., Robbins, W. E., Waters, J. A., Steele, J. E. & Mosettig, E. (1963). *J. Insect Physiol.* **9**, 615–622.

Treherne, J. E. (1958). *J. exp. Biol.* **35**, 297–306.

Waller, J. B. (1965). *Proc. Int. Congr. Ent.* pp. 509–511.

Wigglesworth, V. B. (1963). *J. Insect Physiol.* **9**, 105–119.

Winteringham, F. P. W. (1958). *Int. Congr. Biochem.*, pp. 210–215.

Winteringham, F. P. W. (1960). *Biochem. J.* **75**, 38–45.

Winteringham, F. P. W. (1965). In *Studies in Comparative Biochemistry*. Ed. K. A. Munday, pp. 107–151 Oxford: Pergamon Press.

Winteringham, F. P. W., Bridges, P. M. & Hellyer, G. C. (1955). *Biochem. J.* **59**, 13–21.

Wyatt, G. R. & Kalf, G. F. (1957). *J. gen. Physiol.* **40**, 833–847.

DISCUSSION

S. G. Van den Bergh*: I was very interested in your remarks on the role of amino acids as a fuel for energy supply during flight, especially in your answer to my objections against such a role. I do agree that amino acids may be oxidized without pyruvate being converted into alanine and that glutamate may be formed. But that was not my objection (cf. *Biochem. J.* (1964) **93**, 128). My argument was that isolated flight muscle mitochondria oxidize added amino acids only very slowly as compared with pyruvate or glycerophosphate. From these observations I concluded that if amino acids have any role in energy supply, it is in the formation of Krebs-cycle intermediates by transamination, since a high intramitochondrial level of Krebs-cycle intermediates is necessary for an optimal rate of pyruvate oxidation.

* Laboratory of Biochemistry (formerly Physiological Chemistry), University of Amsterdam, The Netherlands.

5

INTERMEDIARY METABOLISM AND THE
INSECT FAT BODY

By B. A. KILBY

Department of Biochemistry, University of Leeds, England

THE insect fat body is usually one of the most conspicuous organs to be seen when an insect is dissected, since it is generally in the form of glistening sheets of large cells, the colour varying from white to deep yellow. The sheets may be continuous or fenestrated, flat or convoluted, irregularly lobed or ribbon-like, etc., but the arrangement is more or less constant for a given species. Photographs of a selection of different fat bodies are shown in a paper by Buys (1924). The thin sheet-like structure gives a maximum area of contact with the blood and is thus admirably suited for a rapid exchange of metabolites with the blood.

The cytoplasm of fat body cells from a well nourished insect is packed with droplets of fat, glycogen and protein, showing that the tissue serves as an important storage depot for reserve materials. In insects which undergo a complete metamorphosis, the larval stage is largely devoted to the accumulation and storage of nutrients which can be used during the pupal stage for the development of the adult form. The fat body of the mature bee larva, for instance, largely fills the body cavity and makes up 65% of the body weight, and over one-third of the dry weight of the larva is due to glycogen. β-Carotene is frequently stored in the fat body, producing a bright yellow colour. The female locust requires a considerable amount of carotene during egg formation and the pigment must be derived from the food and stored since she is unable to synthesize it. Uric acid is often formed as an end product of nitrogen metabolism and may be stored in the fat body in some insects instead of being excreted. This 'storage excretion' is normally harmless, but it has been shown that if cockroaches are fed on a very high protein diet, the fat body becomes greatly enlarged and crammed with white deposits of uric acid so that the insect may be killed by the abnormal internal accumulations of its own waste (Haydak, 1953).

During the past few years it has become evident that the fat body is not merely a relatively inert organ for storage, but is the site of considerable metabolic activity, and indeed shows some of the functions of the mammalian liver. A brief review will now be made of some of the published work on the intermediary metabolism of fat, carbohydrate, protein and purines in fat body (for a more extensive review, see Kilby, 1963).

39

I. FAT METABOLISM

Most insects are well supplied with fat reserves since data collected together by Fast (1964) show that the mean lipid content of different insect species on a dry basis is around 30% for larvae and 20% for adults, but values of over 80% have been reported for some caterpillars. Insects can readily synthesize fat from non-lipid sources. This was studied in an elegant manner by Wigglesworth (1942) who starved mosquito larvae until the reserves in their fat bodies were exhausted, and then observed the reappearance in the fat bodies of living larvae of fat droplets after feeding the larvae on protein, amino acids or sugars. An interesting difference between the sexes was found by van Handel & Lum (1961) using adult mosquitoes; although the males and females contained a similar amount of fat at the time of emergence, yet after seven days feeding on glucose, the females contained fifty times as much fat as the males, since they were able to synthesize it from glucose whereas the males appeared unable to do so. Van Handel and Lum suggest that a further investigation of this difference between the sexes might throw light upon the physiological control of lipid metabolism.

Working with intact tissue instead of whole animals, Clements (1959) showed that when locust fat body was incubated with labelled glucose or amino acids, labelled fat was formed. Homogenates of fat body were found by Zebe & McShan (1959) and Tietz (1961) to incorporate acetate, and the cofactor requirements (ATP, CoA, NADP, Mg^{++}, CO_2, malonate, etc.) were very similar to those for mammalian liver preparation, suggesting that the same or a similar biosynthetic pathway is used by insects.

It has been established that a number of insects which make long flights—such as the locust—use lipid as the main energy source to sustain the flight muscles, which are very efficient at oxidizing fatty acids (Meyer, Preiss & Bauer, 1960). The main fat reserves are in the fat body, and the question arises as to the chemical form in which the fat is mobilized from the fat body and transported to the flight muscles. The lipase activity of the fat body in the Desert locust was found to be thirty-five times as great as that in the muscles by George & Eapen (1959) who suggested that the fat reserves were hydrolysed in the fat body and the free fatty acids transported to the muscles. Wigglesworth (1958) had previously demonstrated histochemically that each fat droplet in the fat body cells of *Rhodnius* had a little cap with lipase activity and had suggested that these caps might catalyse the reversible hydrolysis of triglycerides. Tietz (1962) found that when carboxyl-labelled palmitate was incubated with locust fat body in a phosphate-saline buffer, there was a ready incorporation into the glyceride fraction, but if the buffer solution was replaced by locust blood, 48% of the labelled glyceride fraction was released into the medium within an hour. A similar release was not obtained when locust blood was replaced by solutions of bovine serum, or bovine or egg albumin. The amount of released glyceride was proportional to the amount of locust blood added, and the suggestion was made that *in vivo* glycerides are mobilized and incorporated into haemolymph lipoprotein, and that they are not transported as free fatty acids. The specific activity of the released glyceride was about ten times that of the glyceride in the fat body tissue, showing that the glycerides recently formed from labelled palmitate were being preferentially released. An explanation of this was afforded by the work of Chino & Gilbert (1964) who examined the chemical nature of the released glycerides by column chromatography and found that almost all the

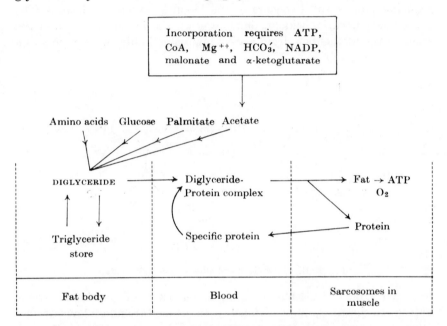

Fig. 1. Summary of fat metabolism in insect fat body.

labelled material was in the diglyceride fraction. Almost 98% of the stored neutral fat in the fat body consists, however, of triglyceride. It would therefore appear that fatty acids are incorporated initially into diglyceride by the fat body (blood shows a negligible incorporation activity) and this diglyceride can either be released into the blood, forming a complex with a specific protein, or else converted into tri-glyceride and stored. During prolonged flight, one would assume that the muscles remove the diglyceride and the level of the diglyceride-protein complex in the blood is maintained by partial hydrolysis of triglyceride in the fat body. It has been estimated that an adult locust oxidizes about 17 mg fat/hr during flight (Weis-Fogh, 1952). The pattern of lipid metabolism is summarized in Fig. 1. Orr, in Baltimore, has shown (1964) that lipid accumulates in the fat body of female flies until yolk formation in the eggs begins, and it then falls, the size of the fat depot probably being under hormonal control. Removal of the corpora allata leads to a massive hypertrophy of the fat body with a four- to fivefold increase in the fat content. The effects of insect hormones on metabolic changes have been reviewed recently (Wigglesworth, 1964).

II. CARBOHYDRATE METABOLISM

The two most important carbohydrates used by insects as energy reserves are trehalose and glycogen. Trehalose is a non-reducing di-saccharide consisting of two α-glucose residues joined through their reducing groups and it occurs in the blood of almost all insects. The concentration varies widely, depending on the insect species and the stage in the life history, from a very low value in blowfly maggots to a

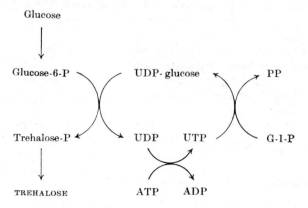

Fig. 2. Biosynthesis of trehalose in locust fat body.

recorded value of 6554 mg/100 ml in a solitary bee larva. Less extreme values are shown by the cockroach with a blood trehalose level around 1000 mg/100 ml or the Desert locust with values up to 1500 mg/100 ml. The blood glucose level, on the other hand, is negligible in comparison as it is usually below 30 mg/100 ml. Treherne (1958) showed that ^{14}C-glucose was absorbed from the gut of locusts and very rapidly and almost completely converted into blood trehalose. Candy & Kilby (1961) showed that this conversion could take place in the fat body and they established that the biosynthetic pathway was the now familiar one involving uridine diphosphate glucose (Fig. 2) which had been established earlier by Cabib & Leloir (1958) for trehalose phosphate formation in yeast.

Clegg & Evans (1961) have shown that most of the energy required by the blowfly *Phormia* for prolonged flight is derived from the oxidation of blood trehalose. The total amount of the sugar in the blood was sufficient for only about 14 min flight, nevertheless the fly was able to keep up sustained flight for 3 hr. The reason for this was that the fat body was able to synthesize trehalose and liberate it into the blood at almost the same rate as it was utilized. There was a small deficiency, however, and after a few hours the blood trehalose level had fallen to about 20% of its initial value and the fly ceased flying through exhaustion. If trehalose was injected, flight could be resumed. Fat body glycogen stores are known to become depleted when insects are flown to exhaustion, so trehalose appears to be synthesized at the expense of glycogen. There is good evidence for the hormonal control of this conversion.

There are groups of cells in the brains of insects which are the source of a hormone, and in the cockroach this material can be seen to pass from

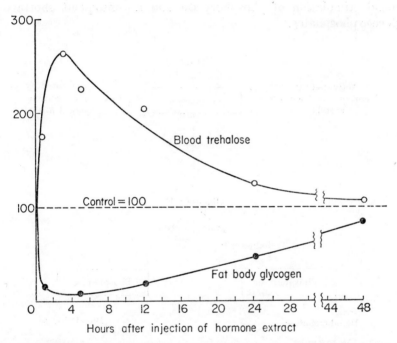

Fig. 3. Changes in blood trehalose level and fat body glycogen stores after injection of an extract of corpora cardiaca. The mean values of the controls taken as 100. (Drawn from data of Steele, 1963.)

the neurosecretory cells along the axons to a paired organ, the corpora cardiaca, in which the secretion is stored prior to release into the blood (Scharrer, 1952). Extracts of the corpora cardiaca can therefore be used as a source of the brain hormone. Steele (1963) and Bowers & Friedman (1963) have shown that injection of such extracts into the cockroach results in a sharp rise in the blood trehalose level and a fall in the fat body glycogen stores. Some of Steele's data have been replotted in Fig. 3, and it will be seen that there is a two and a half fold rise within 5 hr of the injection of hormone, and a simultaneous fall in glycogen, and normal levels are almost regained after 2 days. The rise in blood trehalose was dependent on the amount of hormone extract injected, and even the equivalent of 1/500th of a pair of glands produced a 30% rise. Steele also demonstrated that the phosphorylase activity of isolated fat body was stimulated by the hormone extract—the amount of stimulation varying between 61 and 325% in different experiments. This would lead to an increased supply of glucose phosphates which are the starting materials for trehalose biosynthesis. The same phosphates would also be required at the time of moulting for chitin biosynthesis which takes place through uridine diphosphate N-acetylglucosamine (Candy & Kilby, 1962) and the delay in moulting produced by Pfeiffer (1939) in *Melanoplus* by removal of the corpora cardiaca might be due to the absence of a hormonal stimulation of phosphorylase and a consequent shortage of glucose phosphates.

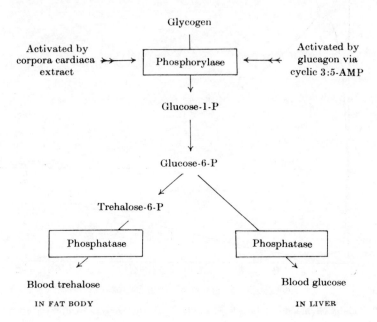

Fig. 4. A comparison of the glycogen to blood sugar pathways in insect fat body and mammalian liver.

The effect of the brain hormone on the blood sugar level in insects shows a close parallel with that of glucagon and catecholamines on mammalian blood sugar level (Fig. 4). In both systems, phosphorylase is stimulated to produce glucose phosphates leading to an increase in blood trehalose or blood glucose. The action of glucagon in liver is to stimulate adenyl cyclase, the enzyme which makes cyclic $3':5'$-AMP, the coenzyme of the kinase which converts inactive phosphorylase b into the active phosphorylase a. It would be interesting to know if a similar mechanism is operative in the invertebrate system.

III. PROTEIN METABOLISM

The fat body is quite an active site for the intermediary metabolism of amino acids. Various transaminases are present so that, for example. at least 16 amino acids will undergo transamination with α-oxoglutarate. Other enzymes reported from the fat body include a leucine/alanine transaminase, D- and L-amino acid oxidases, glutaminase, glutamine synthetase, glutamic dehydrogenase, arginase and serine transhydroxy-methylase. Although the amino acid level in insect blood is much higher than in mammalian blood, no very striking differences in metabolism have been reported.

Shigematsu in Japan (1960) has shown that the fat body can synthesize some of the blood proteins. Silkworm blood contains three main protein components: albumin, globulin I and globulin II. During the growth of the fifth instar of the silkworm, the blood protein level rises from about 2·6 mg/100 ml to 7·3 mg/100 ml, mainly due to an increase in the globulin fractions, equivalent to the appearance of about 14 mg of new protein per day per insect. When silkworm fat body was incubated with ATP and a casein hydrolysate, there was a net synthesis of protein, equivalent to around 12 mg per day. About half of this was secreted into the incubation medium and was shown to be identical electrophoretically with the two blood globulins, but the albumin fraction was absent. If labelled amino acids were used, the specific activity of the protein secreted into the medium was twenty times that of the tissue protein. It appears that protein synthesis in the fat body is controlled by the hormone from the neurosecretory cells of the brain, and that when this is liberated into the blood, the fat body is stimulated to produce protein from the circulating amino acids. If the neurosecretory cells are destroyed, the blood protein level falls to a half or a third of the normal value (Hill, 1962, 1963). Hill found that blood proteins labelled with fluorescein were taken up by developing eggs, so one of the functions of the fat body may be to synthesize protein of amino acids and to supply this ready made to the ovaries during egg development.

IV. PURINE METABOLISM

In 1935, Liefert reported a large increase in uric acid when insect fat body was incubated with malonate and urea, but with the passage of the years and the elucidation of the pathway of purine biosynthesis in birds and animals, this finding appeared increasingly curious. Around 1957, three groups re-examined uric acid formation by fat body. McEnroe & Forgash (1958) found that labelled formate was incorporated into the 2 and 8 positions of the purine ring, Desai & Kilby (1958) found that 4-amino-5-imidazole carboxamide led to a large increase in uric acid formation, while Heller & Jezewska (1959) incubated fat body simultaneously with all the precursors expected if the carboxamide pathway was being followed, and observed a 50–500% increase in uric acid formation. No one was able to show any increased biosynthesis of uric acid from malonate and urea, and there does not appear to be any reason at present to doubt that purine biosynthesis occurs by essentially the same route in liver and fat body.

The enzymes necessary for the conversion of adenine, guanine, hypoxanthine and xanthine into uric acid have been found in insect fat bodies, and uric acid is frequently the major end product of nitrogen metabolism in terrestrial insects. Uricase is not uncommon, however, and uric acid may thus be at least partially converted into allantoin. Thus, in the blowfly larvae, uricase is present in the fat body during early larval life, disappears before pupation and reappears in the adult. During its absence, uric acid accumulates in the fat body.

Symbiotic bacteria occur in special cells (mycetocytes) in the fat body and sometimes elsewhere in certain insects. The bacteria from the cockroach can be cultured in a medium containing uric acid as the sole source of carbon and nitrogen (Keller, 1950). These bacteria have been shown (J. F. Donnellan & B. A. Kilby, 1965, unpublished results) to contain uricase, allantoinase, allantoicase, urease, glyoxalate carboligase and tartronate semialdehyde reductase, so that uric acid can be degraded to ammonia, glycerate and carbon dioxide. The stores of uric acid in the cockroach fat body might thus serve as a nitrogen reserve, to be tapped with the assistance of the bacteria. The cockroach appears to benefit from the presence of its symbiotic bacteria since female cockroaches rendered asymbiotic show degeneration of the ovaries (Glaser, 1946) and it appears reasonable to suppose that the bacteria may supply growth factors to their host. Ascorbate is known to be synthesized by the bacteria, whereas the cockroach fat body cells without bacteria are unable to do this, but it is not clear whether ascorbate is essential to the insect (Pierre, 1962).

Allantoinase and allantoicase have been reported from a few insects, so a fairly extensive degradation of the purine ring may be possible in the absence of bacteria, but since urease has not been found in insects without symbiotic bacteria, it is not clear how the nitrogen could be released. Reduction of uric acid by, for instance, reversal of some of the stages of purine synthesis might make the purine ring available for nucleotide formation or offer an alternative route for further degradation, but experimental evidence is lacking at present.

CONCLUSION

The fat body is seen to be a versatile organ that can synthesize fat, carbohydrates and protein from a variety of substrates and store them ready for mobilization when required as a source of energy or for the building of new tissue. The ability of the fat body to interconvert metabolites is well illustrated by the work of Clements (1959) and Hines & Smith (1963) in which locust fat body was incubated with labelled glycine, leucine, acetate, glucose or succinate, leading to the formation of a wide range of labelled products, including Krebs cycle acids, amino acids, sugars, and fats. Under the influence of hormones, the fat body can regulate the level of blood sugar and probably also of blood protein. Ammonia can be converted into uric acid and other detoxification reactions are carried out—some phenols, for example, are converted into their corresponding β-glucosides by locust fat body.

Mammalian liver and insect fat body thus resemble each other in biochemical function in a number of respects. Patkin & Masoro (1961) have shown that mammalian adipose tissue is responsible for 95% of the fatty acid biosynthesis in the animal, so, as Orr has pointed out, there is an analogy too between the insect fat body and the adipose tissue of higher animals, as both are active sites for lipid metabolism and are no longer to be regarded merely as relatively inert tissues for fat storage. The fat body can play many roles. It is a site of much intermediary metabolism and biosynthesis, a storehouse for nutrients, a regulator of some blood constituents, a location for detoxification and sometimes a dump for waste material and a home for symbionts. It is clearly an organ worthy of further study.

REFERENCES

Bowers, W. S. & Friedman, S. (1963). *Gen. comp. Endocr.* **3**, 46.
Buys, K. S. (1924). *J. Morph.* **38**, 485.
Cabib, E. & Leloir, L. F. (1958). *J. biol. Chem.* **231**, 259.
Candy, D. J. & Kilby, B. A. (1961). *Biochem. J.* **78**, 531.
Candy, D. J. & Kilby, B. A. (1962). *J. exp. Biol.* **39**, 129.
Chino, H. & Gilbert, L. I. (1964). *Science* **143**, 359.
Clegg, J. S. & Evans, D. R. (1961). *J. exp. Biol.* **38**, 771.
Clements, A. N. (1959). *J. exp. Biol.* **36**, 665.
Desai, R. M. & Kilby, B. A. (1958). *Archs. int. Physiol. Biochim.* **66**, 282.
Fast, P. G. (1964). *Mem. ent. Soc. Can.* No. 37.
George, J. C. & Eapen, J. (1959). *J. cell. comp. Physiol.* **54**, 293.
Glaser, R. W. (1946). *J. Parasit.* **32**, 483.
Haydak, M. H. (1953). *Ann. ent. Soc. Am.* **46**, 547.
Heller, J. & Jezewska, M. M. (1959). *Bull. Acad. pol. Sci. Cl. II Sér. Sci. biol.* **7**, 1.
Hill, L. (1962). *J. Insect Physiol.* **8**, 609.
Hill, L. (1963). *The endocrine control of oocyte development in the Desert Locust, Schistocerca gregaria.* Thesis, University of Sheffield, quoted by Wigglesworth (1964).
Hines, W. J. W. & Smith, M. J. H. (1963). *J. Insect Physiol.* **9**, 463.
Keller, H. (1950). *Z. Naturf.* **56**, 269.
Kilby, B. A. (1963). *Adv. Insect Physiol.* **1**, 111.
Liefert, H. (1935). *Zool. Jb. Abt. allg. Zool. Physiol.* **55**, 171.
McEnroe, W. D. & Forgash, A. J. (1958). *Ann. ent. Soc. Am.* **51**, 126.
Meyer, H., Preiss, B. & Bauer, S. (1960). *Biochem. J.* **76**, 27.
Orr, C. W. M. (1964). *J. Insect Physiol.* **10**, 103.
Patkin, J. & Masoro, M. J. (1961). *Am. J. Physiol.* **200**, 847.
Pfeiffer, I. W. (1939). *J. exp. Zool.* **82**, 439.
Pierre, L. L. (1962). *Nature, Lond.* **193**, 904.
Scharrer, B. (1952). *Biol. Bull. mar. biol. Lab., Woods Hole* **102**, 261.
Shigematsu, H. (1960). *Bull. seric. Exp. Stn Japan* **16**, 141.

Steele, J. E. (1963). *Gen. comp. Endocr.* **3**, 46.

Tietz, A. (1961). *J. Lipid Res.* **2**, 182.

Tietz, A. (1962). *J. Lipid Res.* **3**, 421.

Treherne, J. E. (1958). *J. exp. Biol.* **35**, 611.

Van Handel, E. & Lum, P. T. M. (1961). *Science* **134**, 1979.

Weis-Fogh, T. (1952). *Phil. Trans. R. Soc.* B **237**, 1.

Wigglesworth, V. B. (1942). *J. exp. Biol.* **19**, 56.

Wigglesworth, V. B. (1958). *Q. Jl. microsc. Sci.* **99**, 441.

Wigglesworth, V. B. (1964). *Adv. Insect Physiol.* **2**, 247.

Zebe, E. & McShan, W. H. (1959). *Biochim. biophys. Acta* **31**, 513.

THE METABOLISM OF AROMATIC COMPOUNDS

By P. C. J. BRUNET

Department of Zoology, University of Oxford, England

INTRODUCTION

It is not known for certain whether all the major pathways of metabolism of aromatic amino acids in insects have been unearthed, and few have been subjected to detailed scrutiny. Nevertheless such information as there is is not without interest. The highways of metabolism are closely similar in all animals, but what follows may serve as an example to show how the byways are often remarkably different. To anyone familiar only with the metabolism of microorganisms and mammals the insects hold out some surprises.

An attempt will be made to cover the main fields of advance and controversy, and to draw attention to reviews where the field has been covered before. As a good yard-stick of comparison, the work of Henderson, Gholson & Dalgliesh (1962) offers a thoroughgoing account of the metabolism of aromatic compounds in the more familiar organisms. A useful outline of the situation in insects is given in Gilmour (1965).

If it is thought that too much emphasis is given to the occurrence, rather than metabolism of aromatic compounds, it should be realized that the subject of insect biochemistry is relatively young. Isolation and identification generally precedes a dynamic comprehension of any substance, but knowledge of its existence may stimulate the search for its origin and consequences.

REQUIREMENTS AND INTAKE OF AROMATIC AMINO ACIDS

The dietary requirements of an insect, with regard to essential amino acids, resemble those of a mammal, and phenylalanine and tryptophan are among the ten that are required (Lipke & Fraenkel, 1956; Gilmour, 1961; Chen, 1962). All insects for which records exist require these with the exception of the small cockroach (*Blatella*), which can survive without phenylalanine.

Considerable quantities of amino acids are found in insect blood, which may have fifty times the amino acid content of vertebrate blood (Duchâteau & Florkin, 1958). Differences in the state of nutrition can account for some of the changes in proportions of amino acids in the blood at any one time, nevertheless there must be some sparing mechanism that allows tyrosine characteristically to mount up in the blood of larvae prior to pupation (Fraenkel & Rudall, 1947; Florkin & Jeniaux, 1964).

Apart from dietary phenylalanine, tyrosine and tryptophan, it is known that there is a secondary source of supply of aromatic compounds available to at least two insects. Henry (1962) fed [U-^{14}C]glucose to normal specimens of *Blatella*, and to animals that had been rendered free from intracellular symbionts by the method of Brooks & Richards (1955). The normal animals were found to contain the isotope in most of the amino acids, including phenylalanine and tyrosine (tryptophan, if present, would have been destroyed in the extraction procedure), while none was found in the aposymbiotic cockroaches. Brunet (1963a, b) showed that another cockroach (*Periplaneta*) could synthesize 3,4-dihydroxybenzoic acid from [1-^{14}C]glucose. It will be shown later that the integumentary colour of insects is characteristically derived from tyrosine derivatives, and it is interesting to note in Richards & Brooks (1958) that insects freed of their symbionts are typically paler than normal insects. Intracellular symbionts are not present in all orders of insects, and this is reflected in the inability of a dipteran (*Phormia*) and a lepidopteran (*Agrotis*) to synthesize phenylalanine or tyrosine from glucose (Kasting & McGinnis, 1958, 1962).

Conversion of phenylalanine into tyrosine

Hydroxylation of phenylalanine to tyrosine can take place in insects. This is implied by the requirement for phenylalanine but not for tyrosine, and was substantiated by Fukuda (1956), and Bricteux-Grégoire, Verly & Florkin (1956) who isolated radioactive tyrosine from silk produced by larvae that had received injections of [^{14}C]phenylalanine.

The unusual *ortho*-form of tyrosine (Fig. 1) has been reported from the fly, *Calliphora* (Dennell, 1956), and *p*-tyrosine occurs as an *O*-phosphate (Fig. 1) in a lethal mutant of *Drosophila* (Mitchell, Chen & Hadorn, 1960).

THE PRODUCTS OF METABOLISM OF TYROSINE AND PHENYLALANINE AND THEIR BIOLOGICAL FUNCTION

Insect proteins

It goes without saying that insect proteins incorporate aromatic amino acid into their primary structure. There are, however, two families of protein characteristically present in insects that are worthy of special note. Both groups are structural proteins, depending for their stability on the presence of aromatic or quinonoid cross-linkages. The more recently discovered resilins are rubber-like, having unusually perfect elasticity, and serving as rather specialized hinge-joints. The other group, the sclerotins form rigid structures, and provide a solid matrix in the otherwise flexible chitinous cuticle, stiffening it in parts and providing it with protective and mechanical properties. The existence of sclerotins is widespread and has been recognized for twenty-five years but it is still rare to find them mentioned in a general work on proteins.

Resilin—an elastic cross-linked protein

In 1960 Weis-Fogh described a protein that somewhat resembles elastin in its physical properties, but which in other respects, for example the proportions of the constituent amino acids, is different (Bailey & Weis-Fogh, 1961). The name resilin was given to this hyaline, colourless,

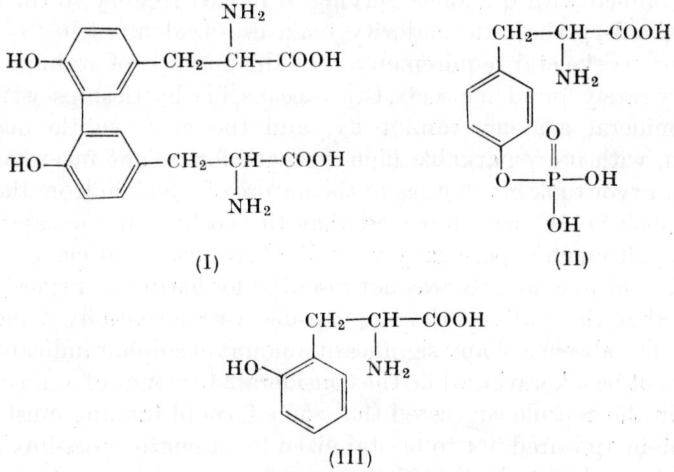

Fig. 1. Unusual amino acids from insects.

(I) Dityrosine from the locust (*Schistocerca*). (II) *Para*-tyrosine-*O*-phosphate from the fruit-fly (*Drosophila*). (III) *Ortho*-tyrosine from the blowfly (*Calliphora*).

elastic protein. It behaves like a swollen, isotropic rubber, and is remarkable for its stability towards denaturing agents and for showing complete lack of flow when under tension, which is without parallel in any other natural or synthetic rubber. From its physical properties it has been concluded that it is a structural protein in which the primary chains show little or no tendency to form secondary structures, having a uniform three-dimensional net-like arrangement with covalent cross-links.

Weis-Fogh (1961a, b) made a very thorough study of the physical properties of resilin, and arrived at an estimate of one cross-link for every hundred or so amino acid residues in the protein. Hydrolysis of resilin yields two fluorescent compounds, a diaminodicarboxylic acid and a triaminotricarboxylic acid (Andersen, 1963), and the amino-groups of these compounds are not available to dinitrofluorobenzene, suggesting that they are incorporated into the peptide sequence. These poly-functional elements evidently provide a basis for the cross-linking. They are now known to be di- and tri-tyrosine (Fig. 1) (Andersen, 1964).

The characteristic properties of resilin are made use of in the flight mechanism of insects. The wings show elastic recoil, and the presence of resilin in the wing-hinges provides for this. Hinges in jaw mechanisms may be of resilin, as are the 'springs' that oppose the muscles that serve the respiratory, ventilatory system in beetles. A valuable summary of the nature of resilin and of its distribution has been published by Andersen & Weis-Fogh (1964).

Sclerotin—a rigid, cross-linked protein

In 1940, Pryor (1940a) put forward the general notion of a protein, heavily tanned with quinones, serving to impart rigidity to the insect. Many animals, perhaps the majority, make use of calcium salts to provide their various skeletal requirements, but this method of stabilization is only very rarely found in insects. Crustaceans, like battleships, with their heavy mineral armour, cannot fly, and the more subtle material, sclerotin, with its remarkable high strength for weight ratio has been evolved. Pryor took his clues as to the nature of sclerotin from the work of Campbell (1929) who reported that the cockroach egg-capsule (or ootheca), although superficially very like hard insect cuticle, contained no chitin: chitin evidently was not essential for hardness. Pryor (1940a) showed that the walls of the egg-capsule were essentially a modified protein. The absence of any significant amount of sulphur indicated that it could not be a keratin, while the considerable amount of o-dihydroxy-phenol in the capsule suggested that some form of tanning must occur. The protein appeared not to be stabilized by aromatic cross-linking but rather by covalent links provided by o-quinones.

Extending his idea to insect cuticle (1940b), Pryor demonstrated that the three requirements for sclerotin formation were present, namely, a tannable protein, the precursor of an o-quinone, and an oxidase system. The essentials of this explanation have stood the test of time and it remains acceptable, although the exact relationship between quinone and protein has yet to be discovered. Pryor (1962) has recently published a reassessment of the situation.

The process of sclerotization is a very striking one: over a period of hours, the insect cuticle, which, immediately after moulting, is pure white and tender, undergoes complete alteration, changing in texture and often also in colour. Pryor believed that the two processes, hardening and darkening, were necessarily associated, but while this is commonly so it is not always so.

Available information, particularly from industrial tanning (see Gustavson, 1949, 1956), indicated that quinones would react, in the absence of sulphydryl-groups, with the amino-groups of a protein. This was confirmed in the case of sclerotin by blocking the free amino-groups, which led to subsequent failure of the protein to harden (Pryor, 1940a, b); sclerotin could therefore be regarded as a fibrous protein, three-dimensionally knit together by covalent bonding through amino-groups to quinones formed as the result of enzymic oxidation of o-dihydroxy-phenols.

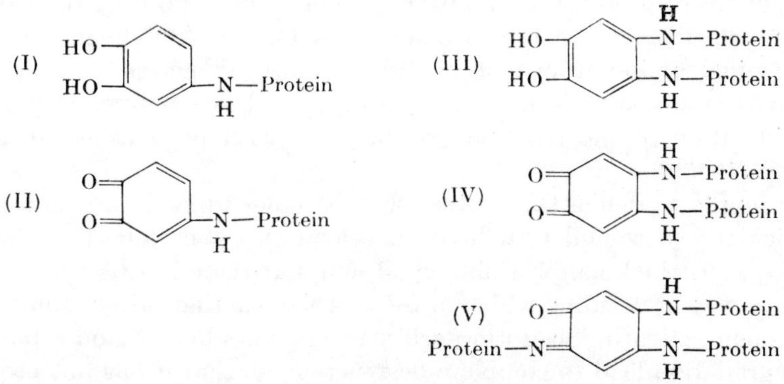

(I) HO—⟨ ⟩—HO ——N—Protein
                      H

(II) O=⟨ ⟩=O ——N—Protein
                 H

(III) HO—⟨ ⟩—N—Protein (H); HO——N—Protein
                                    H

(IV) O=⟨ ⟩=O ——N—Protein (H); N—Protein
                               H

(V) O=⟨ ⟩ N—Protein (H); Protein—N= ——N—Protein
                                        H

Fig. 2. Sequence (I–V) of products formed as a result of the reactions between quinones and proteins (based on Hackman and Mason). The reaction mechanism is shown in Fig. 3.

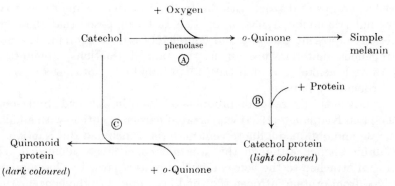

Fig. 3. Relationship between the components of a quinone-tanning system (after Mason).

Quinone tanning

Directing their attention to the quinones derivable from insect o-dihydroxyphenols, Hackman & Todd (1953) showed that these would react with amino-compounds forming mono- and di-aminoquinones (Fig. 2, II, IV) and diaminoquinoneimines (Fig. 2, V), all of which are coloured. Mason (1955a, b) went on to show that the reaction takes place step-wise: catechol in the presence of a phenolase is oxidized to o-quinone (Fig. 3, stage A). This quinone can then combine with a protein by way of an amino-group to give a catechol-protein (Fig. 2, I, Fig. 3, stage B). If excess o-quinone is being generated by stage A, this will oxidize the

6

catechol-protein to a quinonoid-protein (Fig. 2, II, Fig. 3, stage C) with concomitant reductive re-formation of catechol. Quinonoid-proteins formed in this way are coloured but catechol proteins are not, which provides an explanation of the nature of hardened, pale-coloured cuticle. o-Quinones react in a similar way with sulphydryl-compounds (Mason, 1955b) but it has been shown that cuticular protein is virtually free from sulphur (Pryor, 1940b; Hackman, 1953a). The rate at which amino-compounds or proteins react with o-quinone is influenced by the nature of the substituents on the nitrogen-atom (Mason & Peterson, 1955): N-terminal amino-groups of peptides showing heightened reactivity towards o-quinones, while ε-lysyl groups are less reactive. Extensive consideration of the reactions of quinones with proteins is given in Mason (1955b).

Attempts to define the protein that becomes tanned have not been particularly successful. Cuticle contains a number of proteins (Hackman, 1953a, b, c; Hackman & Goldberg, 1958), but there has been no satisfactory way of deciding which of these is the one that, after tanning, is to become sclerotin. Sclerotin itself is firmly cross-linked, and attempts at degradation lead to complete destruction, so that it has not proved possible to relate sclerotin to any of the proteins found in cuticle prior to sclerotization. Trim (1941) showed that cuticle protein could be divided into three categories, water-soluble, alkali-soluble and insoluble. The first has groups that react with dinitrofluorobenzene while the last two have not (Hackman, 1953a, b, c). It is to be supposed that these two fractions represent partially and completely tanned protein. The non-nitrogenous material, present in the tanned fractions, amounts to 10–15%; Fraenkel & Rudall (1947) had found 5·8% of this component in hardened fly puparia.

A study of the degradation products of sclerotin was made by Dennell (1958) and Kennaugh (1958) who treated hardened cuticle with alkaline stannite and obtained a fluorescent material which had the reactions of an amino-phenol, although this was not conclusively identified. The nitrogen attached to the benzene nucleus was regarded as having been derived from protein nitrogen that had been linked to the benzene ring. Hackman & Goldberg (1963) did not however find any such material after treating cockroach egg-capsules with stannite.

Cases where suspected quinone tanning has occurred in the absence of detectable free o-dihydroxyphenols have been reported particularly from animals other than insects (Brown, 1950). To explain this occurrence it has been suggested that autotanning of the protein occurs, tyrosyl groups being involved in the cross-linking. There is at present no reason to believe that this does occur in insects, and it is unlikely to on steric grounds, but in as much as tyrosyl groups can be oxidized in situ (Yasonobu, 1959), autotanning must be regarded as a possibility. Hackman (1953c) reported that dialysed insect cuticular proteins were oxidized in vitro by a phenolase.

Though information on the mechanism of quinone-tanning is still very incomplete, such evidence as there is is consistent with the hypothesis that sclerotin is a modified protein cross-linked and rendered extremely stable by the oxidation products of phenolic substances. It is sterically unlikely that one quinone would form the link between two protein chains, and for this reason, and taking into account the brittleness of the material and its high quinone content, it seems probable that sclerotin consists of a meshwork of protein linked at intervals to quinones which form part of a mass of polymerized quinone that fills the interstices between the protein chains (Pryor, 1962).

Quinone-tanning agents

Pryor's work set in train a search for o-dihydroxyphenols in hardened structures both in insects and in other organisms (Brown, 1950), but there were already at that time existing reports of such compounds:

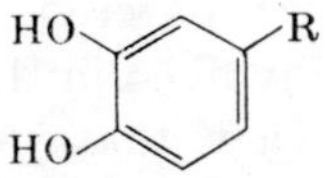

$$HO{-}\text{[benzene ring]}{-}R$$
$$HO{-}$$

*$R_1 = -COOH$ $R_3 = -CH_2-CH-COOH$ *$R_5 = -CH_2-CH_2$
$|$ $|$
OH $NHCOCH_3$

$R_2 = -CH_2-COOH$ $R_4 = -CH_2-CH_2$ *$R_6 = -CH-CH_2$
$|$ $|$ $|$
NH_2 OH $NHCOCH_3$

Fig. 4. Substances claimed to act as precursors of quinone-tanning agents. When substituted with R1—o-dihydroxybenzoic acid; R2—o-dihydroxyphenylacetic acid; R3—o-dihydroxyphenyllactic acid; R4—o-dihydroxyphenylethylamine (Dopamine); R5—N-acetyl-o-dihydroxyphenylethylamine (N-acetyldopamine); R6—N-acetyl-o-dihydroxyphenylethanolamine (N-acetyl-noradrenalin). Also found as 4—O—glucoside.

Schmalfuss & Barthmeyer (1930, 1931) had surveyed the 'chromogens' of arthropods and reported that 81% of the 341 species examined had given a general reaction (ferric chloride) for o-dihydroxyphenols; and 3,4-dihydroxyphenylacetic acid (Fig. 4) had been identified in extracts made from a number of beetles (Schmalfuss, 1937; Schmalfuss, Heider & Winklemann, 1933). The range of known 3,4-dihydroxyphenols was extended by the work of Pryor, Russell & Todd (1946, 1947): the egg-capsule of a cockroach (*Blatta*) and a blowfly larva (*Calliphora*) yielded 3,4-dihydroxybenzoic acid, while the lactic and acetic acids (Fig. 4) were found in a beetle (*Tenebrio*). Later Hackman, Pryor & Todd (1948) again found dihydroxyphenylacetic acid in a number of insects (a locust (*Locusta*) and six beetles). 3,4-Dihydroxybenzoic acid was found in the egg-capsule of another cockroach (*Periplaneta*) by Brunet & Kent (1955a) and in still other cockroaches by Stay & Roth (1962). The range of insects from which dihydroxyphenolic compounds could be extracted has been extended by Kawase (1958), Vercauteren, Aerts & Decleir

(1960), Malek (1961), Sapag-Hagar, González-González & Stamm-Menéndez (1961), and by Tomino (1965).

Caution should be exercised before accepting these results: in some cases identification is far from certain, depending on limited chromatographic procedures; in other cases, where the identifications satisfy all requirements, the methods used by workers have clearly failed to detect all dihydroxyphenols, and others than those described have been shown subsequently to be present in substantial quantities. Nevertheless it can be concluded that o-dihydroxyphenolic carboxylic acids are present in many insects and are possible sources of tanning quinones.

For a number of reasons, the most trenchant being that since o-dihydroxyphenolic acids are fairly easily extractable from cuticle so that they cannot have been involved in a tanning process that involves them in covalent linkage, Dennell and his collaborators offered a new line of explanation (Dennell, 1958): p-quinones were the tanning agents, while the o-compounds, after enzymic oxidation, served only to oxidize the p-compounds. The p-quinones entered the sclerotin, and the o-quinones did not, being only involved in the coupled oxidation process. Malek (1961) accepted the view that p-quinones were involved in cuticles where a darkening of colour accompanied hardening (as in the cockroach), but added the rider that tanning by o-quinones could occur and lead to pale, hardened structures (as in the locust); he also reported free catechol in the locust. The evidence for tanning by p-quinones is sparse and the theory has come up for criticism from a number of quarters (Hackman, 1964); indeed supporting *in vitro* experiments were carried out under very unbiological conditions and have proved to be unrepeatable (Aerts, Vercauteren & Decleir, 1960), while Karlson (1960) has shown that isotopically labelled hydroquinone is not incorporated into cuticle.

As a result of a completely different approach to the subject, Karlson, Sekeris and their collaborators have reached very different conclusions from those set out above. Their extensive work has involved establishing the pathways of tyrosine metabolism and studying the fate of injected ^{14}C-labelled metabolites. They have shown that, prior to the formation of a new cuticle, tyrosine metabolism (see p. 61) in the larva of the blowfly (*Calliphora*) is switched towards the production of N-acetyldopamine (Fig. 4), which they consider to be the chief tanning agent of insect cuticle (Karlson & Sekeris, 1962b; Karlson & Herrlich, 1965).

Since Pryor's early work (1940a, b) it had been accepted that prevention of indole formation was a prerequisite for sclerotization, and it was supposed that this condition would be fulfilled by deamination (a common metabolic process) rather than by N-acylation (for which there was no precedent). However in this respect an N-acetyl compound is certainly as eligible a tanning agent as a phenolic carboxylic acid.

Karlson & Sekeris (1962b) also reported N-acetyldopamine from the mealworm (*Tenebrio*), and its synthesis from tyrosine has subsequently been followed in the locust (*Schistocerca*) (Karlson & Herrlich, 1965). The authentic substance was synthesized by Karlson, Sekeris & Sekeri (1962). *N*-Acetyldopamine has more recently been reported from the egg-shells of a range of insects by Furneaux & McFarlane (1965). Other evidence in support of the theory (that *N*-acetyldopamine is the chief tanning agent of the insects on which they worked) is provided by the pattern of synthesis and disappearance of this compound: it is not produced in the early part of the last larval stage, but later under the influence of the moulting hormone, ecdysone, its synthesis takes place and it mounts up in the body; immediately before and during puparium formation it is rapidly used up. Additional support comes from the findings of Karlson & Liebau (1961) who have extracted a crystalline preparation of phenolase, supposedly responsible for the oxidation of the cuticular *o*-dihydroxyphenol, which acts specifically on catechol-amines, *N*-acetylcatecholamines and on dopa. It scarcely brings about oxidation of monohydroxyphenols and shows no activity towards dihydroxyphenolic acids (except dopa).

N-Acetyldopamine and its precursors are all incorporated into the puparial cuticle if injected into late last-stage larvae: [U-^{14}C]tyrosine, [α-^{14}C]tyrosine and [α-^{14}C]dopa are incorporated into cuticle to an extent of 80%, at the same time [^{14}C]leucine is incorporated only to an extent of 5–10%, which is taken to indicate the involvement of amino acids in cuticular protein (Karlson, 1960). [α-^{14}C]Tyramine and [α-^{14}C]-dopamine were rapidly incorporated (Karlson, Sekeris & Sekeri, 1962), while virtually all the radioactivity was found in the cuticle after injection of [α-^{14}]-*N*-acetyldopamine or [^{14}C-acetyl]-*N*-acetyldopamine (Karlson & Sekeris, 1962b). It might be worth pointing out here that the German authors use the symbol β when referring to the carbon of an amino acid to which the amino-group is attached; English convention uses the symbol α for this. [^{14}C]Hydroquinone was not taken into the cuticle of *Calliphora*, nor was injected [^{14}C]-3,4-dihydroxyphenyl-propionic acid taken up by locust cuticle.

These findings are consistent with the view that *N*-acetyldopamine is the tanning agent, and do not support the claims that the puparium is tanned with *p*-quinones (Dennell, 1958), or by 3,4-dihydroxybenzoic acid (Pryor *et al.*, 1947). With so much convincing evidence, it is extremely probable that Karlson's explanation of the situation in *Calliphora* and *Schistocerca* is correct. However the *ex cathedra* statement of Karlson & Sekeris (1962b) that all insect cuticles are tanned in this way requires more experimental proof before it is acceptable. They regard 3,4-dihydroxyphenolic acids as stray metabolic products arising from the hydroxylation of metabolites on the degradative pathway of tyrosine (see p. 61), but whether this is so or not requires further proof.

The reverse of the situation certainly applies in the case of the egg-capsule of the cockroaches, *Blatta* and *Periplaneta* [and Karlson & Sekeris (1962b) are prepared to accept this]: the tanning agent is

unquestionably 3,4-dihydroxybenzoic acid (Pryor *et al.*, 1946; Brunet &
Kent, 1955a; Kent & Brunet, 1959), with only a trace of an *N*-acetyl-
catecholamine, in this case, *N*-acetyl*nor*adrenalin (Fig. 4) (Brunet, Pau
& Whitehead, 1965, unpublished). The dihydroxyphenolase that is
present in this system acts on carboxylic acids (except dopa) but not
on unacetylated catecholamines (Whitehead, Brunet & Kent, 1960).

The question of melanin

The colour of hardened insect cuticle may range from pure white to
pitch black. If the optical effects that give rise to whiteness are eliminated, cuticles are found that range from parchment colour to black. The
biologist would like to know what underlies such differential pigmentation, both between related species and within one species. Such differences can be extremely relevant to biological problems affecting as they
do such aspects as predator–prey relationships, and physiological
processes such as heat-exchange. One of the most penetrating studies of
the mechanism of evolution (Kettlewell, 1958) involves the study of the
relative extent of dark pigmentation in moths living in industrial and
open habitats. The dark pigment of locusts has a very different distribution in the various phases adopted by the locust (Goodwin, 1950;
Nickerson, 1956) and the nature of this pigmentation is of considerable
interest in this context.

What is the nature of the difference between, to take a simple example,
the white parts of the wing and their black tips in the cabbage butterfly
(*Pieris*)? The black and white colours might be a result of the state of
oxidation of the tanned proteins of the cuticle: catechol-proteins are
pale, quinone-proteins dark; but, although there is all too little con-
cerning this aspect of the subject in the literature, it would appear that
quinone-proteins are only black if two conditions are fulfilled, namely
when dopa is the chromogen, and when the protein has sulphydryl-
groups for attachment to the chromogen, as the quinones derived from
dopa do not attach themselves to the amino-groups of protein (Mason,
1959); other quinone-tanned proteins are dark, but not black (Hackman
& Todd, 1953). Insofar as insect cuticular protein has no free sulphydryl-
groups, a black colour in hardened cuticle cannot directly result from the
tanning of the protein by an oxidation product of dopa. It remains
reasonable to interpret the shade of brown as a result of the state of
oxidation of the tanned protein. We are left to suppose that where the
cuticle is black this must be the result of incorporation of the oxidation
products of dopa as a supplementary pigment, not directly attached
to the protein, but in a polymerized form, either pure or co-polymerized
with the excess tanning quinone.

A number of observations have been made on the processes of hardening and darkening indicating that they are distinct. Waddington (1941)
analysed a range of *Drosophila* races in terms of two processes that

occurred at different times and which could be interpreted as sclerotization and melanization; Goodwin (1952) distinguished these two processes in the locust; and Dennell (1958) showed that the formation of the dark bars on the puparium of *Protophormia* was independent of, and could be inhibited without affecting, sclerotization. Karlson & Schlossberger-Raecke (1962) have reported that the sclerotization process in normal and albino locusts is identical, with the implication that melanization is a separate process that could be lacking without having any effect on sclerotization; and a similar conclusion was reached by Malek (1957). After injecting [^{14}C]tyrosine into crickets, Fuzeau-Braesch (1960) showed that there is first a general uptake of a tyrosine derivative into newly formed cuticle, and following that an enhancement of radioactivity in regions of pigmentation. Cottrell (1964) has clearly shown that the hardening of emerging blowflies (*Calliphora*) takes place considerably before the appearance of black pigment. This temporal separation of the two processes could be engineered in the epidermal cells by a shutting off of the acetylation or deamination system (whichever applies) before completion of cuticle formation, with the result that dopa is to a greater or lesser extent passed out into the cuticle and oxidized there in the final stages.

It would seem that this is the most likely explanation of differential darkening, but there are other possibilities: it has been shown that tyrosyl groups can be oxidized *in situ* in protein (Yasonobu, 1959; Harley-Mason, 1960); if proteins with internal or C-terminal tyrosyl groups are oxidized they have an absorption spectrum like that of oxidized catechol, but with N-terminal tyrosyl groups the spectrum is like that of melanin. However, such cuticular proteins as have been examined possess no N-terminal tyrosine (Hackman, 1953b). Dityrosyl groups in protein (Andersen, 1964) are also potentially melanogenic, providing, as they would, a site to which indole quinones could be attached. Yet again there is the possibility that what has come to be known as melanin may in certain instances be derived from ommochrome pigments (p. 70) (Pryor, 1962).

METABOLISM OF TYROSINE AND PHENYLALANINE

The facts that are known about tyrosine metabolism may represent only an incomplete account of the process as a whole, but they are sufficient to show that an insect makes use of tyrosine in a way that differs markedly from its utilization in a mammal (see Henderson *et al.*, 1962). Tyrosine metabolism varies cyclically, in relation to the repetitive formation of new cuticle. Between each moult it would appear that there is at first a degradative phase, followed by a constructive phase during which aromatic compounds are retained in the body. At such a time 80% of injected [^{14}C]tyrosine is recoverable from newly formed cuticle, which is in marked contrast to the observation of Dalgliesh & Tabechian (1956) that 40% of the tyrosine, injected into a rat is traceable as carbon dioxide within 4 hr. There has been a tendency to focus attention on the constructive aspect of tyrosine metabolism, and less is known about degradation, particularly in the final stages.

The constructive phase

Pryor's discovery (1940a, b) that *o*-dihydroxyphenols are implicated in the formation of cuticle pointed to tyrosine as the most likely source of these compounds. This has been amply borne out. Fraenkel & Rudall (1947) showed that before the onset of pupation, the larval blowfly (*Sarcophaga*) builds up a large reserve of tyrosine in the blood, expending this later during pupation, and Ohnishi (1954a) reported the same situation in the larva of the fruit-fly (*Drosophila*). These findings were taken to be indicative of the usage of tyrosine derivatives in cuticle formation. More definite evidence came from Karlson (1959, 1960) who showed that [^{14}C]tyrosine and dopa are incorporated into cuticle of *Calliphora* to an extent far exceeding that of normal protein synthesis (using leucine as an indicator of this); derivatives of tyramine and dopamine are also incorporated (Karlson, 1962b; Karlson & Sekeris, 1962b). Similar results were obtained with the locust (*Schistocerca*) (Karlson & Herrlich, 1965). Fuzeau-Braesch (1960) has shown that there is incorporation of [^{14}C]tyrosine into the cuticle of the cricket (*Gryllus*), and Brunet (1963a, b) reported incorporation into the tanning agent of the cockroach (*Periplaneta*) egg-capsule. There is little doubt that tyrosine derivatives are deeply bound up with sclerotization of the cuticle.

The pathway of constructive metabolism in *Calliphora* and *Schistocerca*, based on works published by Karlson, Sekeris and their co-workers, is shown in Fig. 5. Apparently hydroxylation takes place first (this aspect will come in for consideration later), and dopa is produced, followed by decarboxylation to dopamine, which is then *N*-acetylated (Karlson, 1962a; Sekeris & Karlson, 1962).

A dopa-decarboxylase has been isolated by Sekeris (1963a). It requires pyridoxal phosphate and iron, and shows preferential activity towards dopa, and to some extent to 5-hydroxytryptophan, but is without activity towards phenylalanine, tyrosine or tryptophan, from which it is concluded that hydroxylation of tyrosine to dopa precedes other changes. Decarboxylase activity depends on the rise in ecdysone concentration in the blood that takes place prior to moulting, but the enzyme is not directly activated by the hormone, which, it is believed, affects synthesis of the enzyme (Karlson & Sekeris, 1962a).

Acetylation of dopamine follows decarboxylation: Karlson & Ammon (1963) isolated an acetyl-CoA-transacetylase that will acetylate tyramine, dopamine and some other amines, but not tyrosine, dopa or glucosamine. The activity of this enzyme is not affected by ecdysone. With its amino-group hindered from forming an indole compound

(Karlson *et al.*, 1962), *N*-acetyldopamine is passed into the cuticle where, after oxidation, it serves as the tanning agent.

While this situation prevails in the case of the two insects cited, and

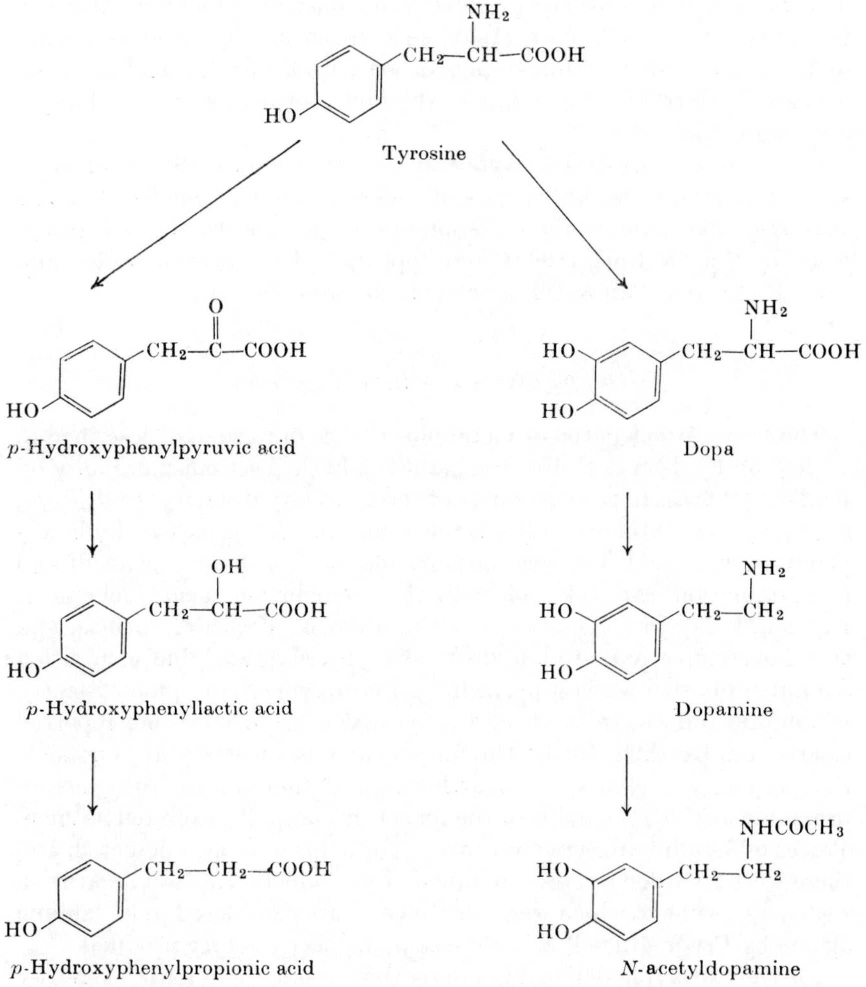

Fig. 5. The two pathways of tyrosine metabolism in the blowfly (*Calliphora*) and the locust (*Schistocerca*). After Karlson, Sekeris and others. The left-hand (acid) metabolism takes place early in the inter-moult period. The right-hand (amine) metabolism takes place before a moult and results in the synthesis of the tanning agent *N*-acetyldopamine. The change-over is brought about by a rise in concentration of the hormone, ecdysone, in the blood.

probably in the beetle (*Tenebrio*), which has also been shown to synthesize *N*-acetyldopamine (Karlson & Sekeris, 1962b), there must be a different scheme of metabolism in the adult cockroach where 3,4-dihydroxybenzoic acid is the tanning agent. This substance is certainly derived from tyrosine: the radioactivity of injected [U-^{14}C]tyrosine, but not [α-^{14}C]tyrosine, can subsequently be detected in the tanning acid (Brunet, 1963a, b); but the intervening stages are unknown. There is the possibility that deamination takes place as in the degradative pathway (see the following section) together with hydroxylation, or that the benzoic acid could be an ultimate product of the constructive amine-pathway: Imaizumi, Yoshida & Kita (1958) recognized 3,4-dihydroxybenzaldehyde in the excreta of guinea-pigs dosed with adrenalin, and Karlson, Sekeris & Herrlich (1963) found this substance in a case of human phaeochromocytoma.

Often a second 3,4-dihydroxyphenol is present, but usually in relatively small amounts, in several species of cockroach, in the colleterial glands that are responsible for the secretion of the egg-capsule; this was recognized by Stay & Roth (1962), and appears to be N-acetyl*nor*adrenalin (Fig. 4) (Brunet, Pau & Whitehead, 1965, unpublished).

Degradative metabolism of tyrosine

The two distinct paths of metabolism (Fig. 5) were first described in outline by Karlson & Hoffmeister (1961) and then set out more fully by Karlson (1962a). In the early part of the third larval stage of *Calliphora*, it was shown that there is active transamination of tyrosine to p-hydroxyphenylpyruvic acid. The enzyme is pyridoxal phosphate-dependent and transamination can take place with α-oxoglutaric acid (Sekeris & Karlson, 1962). In *Schistocerca*, likewise, there is a degradative phase and tyrosine is converted into p-hydroxyphenylpyruvic acid, but in addition a number of other acids supposedly, p-hydroxyphenylpropionic, -lactic, -cinammic and -acetic acids and p-hydroxybenzoic acid were reported (Karlson & Herrlich, 1965). The fate of these is uncertain. It is possible that they are excreted without further degradation: if p-hydroxyphenylpropionic acid is injected into the locust, it is rapidly excreted as such. Traces of 3,4-dihydroxyphenyl carboxylic acids were also detected, and these were regarded as stray metabolic by-products. Karlson regards all such acids, some of which were isolated and are considered to be tanning agents by Pryor, Russell & Todd (see p. 55), as excretory products.

2,5-Dihydroxyphenolic compounds that are characteristic excretory products in vertebrates have not been found in insects.

Hormonal control

An interesting situation is provided by the observation that (if one will accept Karlson's generalization as valid) cuticles, the phenols for which are synthesized by young (not adult) insects, are tanned by substituted catecholamines, while egg-capsules, whose components are secreted by the adult insect, are tanned by a phenolic acid. The early larva, we have seen, metabolizes phenolic carboxylic acids, the late larva, amines. In the early larva neotenin, the juvenile hormone, is present in high concentration, and ecdysone, the moulting hormone, is present in low concentration: the neotenin/ecdysone ratio is high and acids are metabolized. In the late larva the ecdysone concentration rises, the neotenin/ecdysone ratio is low and amines are metabolized.

In this context it is curious to find that Willis & Brunet (see Brunet, 1963a) have shown that the cockroach will only synthesize 3,4-dihydroxybenzoic acid if the corpora allata, that secrete neotenin, are intact. The hormonal situation (a high neotenin/ecdysone ratio) in the adult cockroach is thus similar to that in the early larva, and it is interesting to see that the phenolic tan is correspondingly an acid.

It is not beyond the bounds of possibility therefore that control of metabolism of the bifunctional amino acid tyrosine may depend, like so many fundamental situations in insects (Wigglesworth, 1964), on the interplay of the two chief hormones, neotenin and ecdysone.

The oxidation of phenols

Phenol oxidases have been recognized since the end of the last century and insect material was used by Raper (1928) and his colleagues in delineating the pathway of melanogenesis, but the situation in insects still remains confused. Early work involved the use of crude homogenates that may have contained several enzymes. Lately purer (even crystalline) preparations have been effected, and some very precise information about individual enzymes has been obtained. But information is still lacking as to how many phenol oxidases are present in any one insect, and how and when they are active. An extensive account of the phenolases has been given by Mason (1955b), and their role in insect ecdysis is considered in Cottrell (1964).

There is definitely not one but a range of phenolases in insects: the mechanism of activation of the enzyme in grasshopper eggs (*Melanoplus*) differs markedly from the activation in mealworm (*Tenebrio*) larvae (Bodine & Allen, 1941); the specificity of the phenolase in *Calliphora* (Karlson & Liebau, 1961) differs markedly from the specificity of the tanning enzyme in *Periplaneta* (Whitehead *et al.*, 1960) and *Tenebrio* (Aerts & Vercauteren, 1964), each being 'tailored' for its characteristic natural substrate.

The necessity for activation has been repeatedly reported. Horowitz & Fling (1955) and Ohnishi (1953, 1954b) found this to be so in *Drosophila* and in the fly (*Musca*) (Ohnishi, 1958, 1959). Activation appeared to be an autocatalytic process, an explanation that also seemed to explain Karlson & Schweiger's (1961) findings with regard to *Calliphora*. Later it was shown that when highly purified enzyme and activator are used this is not so (Schweiger & Karlson, 1962; Mergenhagen, 1964).

The situation appears to be as follows: a pre-dihydroxyphenolase is localized in the blood, and a peptide activator in the cells of the epidermis. The activator depends on the presence of ecdysone both for initiation and maintenance of its synthesis (Karlson & Schweiger, 1961). The diphenolase activity of the enzyme is one hundred times as great as the monophenolase activity. However the phenolase will bind to mitochondria, and under these circumstances it shows high monophenolase activity (Karlson, Mergenhagen & Sekeris, 1964; Sekeris & Mergenhagen, 1964). They assume that binding results in some coupling with the hydrogen transport system, and it is interesting to note that this requirement for monophenolase activity was stipulated by Mason, Fowlks & Peterson in 1955.

Lewis (1962) has reported that dopa-oxidase activity in *Drosophila* is under the control of four genes; one structural gene affecting qualitative aspects, and three regulator genes affecting quantity.

Phenolic glucosides

A clear-cut distinction between insects and vertebrates seems to lie in the use of glucosides by insects in situations where the vertebrates use glucuronides. Insects use glucosides both for detoxication and for 'masking' reactive groups.

Myers & Smith (1954) were the first to report that introduced aromatic compounds are converted into β-D-glucosides; more recently Smith (1962) has reviewed the whole subject, and it is further dealt with by Winteringham in this volume (p. 35).

At much the same time, other β-D-glucosides were shown to be naturally occurring substances, the glucoside of 3,4-dihydroxybenzoic acid being found in cockroaches (*Blatta* and *Periplaneta*) by Brunet & Kent (1955a, b; Kent & Brunet, 1959), as well as some other unidentified ones by Stay & Roth (1962). The glucoside of *N*-acetyldopamine was first reported (Okubo, 1958) from a mutant of the fruit-fly (*Drosophila*), and later from the blowfly (*Calliphora*) by Karlson (1962a) and Karlson *et al.* (1962). Rhodommatin (see Fig. 6, p. 68) has proved to be a glucosidic pigment (Butenandt, Biekert, Kübler, Linzen & Traub, 1963), and the ester, benzoylglucoside, has been reported from a cockroach by Quilico, Piozzi, Pavan & Mantica (1959).

The implication of uridine diphosphate glucose in the synthesis of phenolic glucosides has been shown by Trivelloni (1960), Dutton & Duncan (1960), Smith & Turbert (1961) and Dutton (1962), and this aspect is considered by Kilby in this volume (p. 42).

The tanning agent of cockroach egg-capsules is retained in the body until needed, in the form of its β-D-glucoside, which is not subject to oxidation by phenolase. The release of the aglycone precedes sclerotization (Brunet & Kent, 1955a). It would seem that a similar explanation applies in the case of the tanning agent of the adult blowfly (*Calliphora*) (Sekeris, 1964).

Pharmacologically active substances

Catecholamines have been shown to be richly present in insect tissues (Östlund, 1954; Dresse, Jeniaux & Florkin, 1960); however it has never been substantiated that they serve a hormonal or neurohumoral function (Colhoun, 1963a, 1964), although claims that they do so have been made; these are considered in Davey (1964). It is perhaps not surprising that catecholamines have been found in view of the part that they play in sclerotization (see p. 56). Where catecholamines serve a neurohumoral function it is usual to find amine oxidase in association with the nervous system, but Blaschko, Colhoun & Frontali (1961) found no significant amount of this enzyme in a cockroach.

Naturally occurring halogenated aromatic compounds appear to be absent from insects.

MISCELLANEOUS AROMATIC AND QUINONOID COMPOUNDS

A number of compounds have been isolated from insects, and venomous, defensive or pigmentary functions have been attributed to them. Their metabolic origins are largely or entirely unknown. It is likely that some are derived from tyrosine, but in other cases their origin may be exogenous.

An account of the chemistry of nasutins from termites has recently been given (Moore, 1964); they are related to ellagic acid. *p*-Benzoquinone and a number of derivatives are well known, mostly from beetles and cockroaches (Alexander & Barton, 1943; Roth & Stay, 1958); they prove to be a nuisance to man as they can make foodstuffs unpalatable. Quinones are present in the remarkable defensive secretion of the beetle (*Brachinus*) that decrepitates on emission (Schildknecht, 1957). These substances are considered in a review by Pavan (1959).

Anthraquinones occur but rarely in insects, being present as highly coloured substances (such as cochineal, the lake of which is carmine, and several other natural dyes). Other polycyclic quinones occur as dark pigments in aphids (Brown, Ekstrand, Johnson, MacDonald & Todd, 1952). Many of these quinones are glucosidic. Accounts of the structure and distribution of insect quinones are given in Thomson (1957) and Gilmour (1961).

A flavone (probably derived from the food plant) was extracted from a butterfly (*Melanargia*) by Thompson (1926). Anthoxanthins are also present in a small number of other Lepidoptera (Ford, 1941; Davies, 1964).

METABOLIC PATHWAYS AND PRODUCTS OF TRYPTOPHAN

The pattern of employment of tryptophan in insects is characteristic and has a distinctly different emphasis from the pattern of use in other animals. Henderson *et al.* (1962) recognize four main pathways: (i) oxidation to formylkynurenine, (ii) hydroxylation to 5-hydroxytryptophan, (iii) conversion into indole-3-acetic acid, and (iv) fission to indole. The last two are only known to occur in plants and micro-organisms, but not in animals, and insects provide no exception to this. The first two pathways are represented in insects. Very little is known about the 5-hydroxytryptophan pathway, but hydroxyindolealkylamines are evidently present and active in the neuromuscular system. The first pathway, leading on from formylkynurenine is greatly emphasized in insects: kynurenine is converted, so far as is known, in all (non-mutant) insects to ommochrome pigments, which are not known in vertebrates. There is some circumstantial evidence, discussed below (p. 71), that virtually all tryptophan is channelled into the production of these pigments: it appears that none is converted into nicotinic acid, and, although there has been no inquiry as to whether tryptophan can undergo complete degradation, such evidence as there is seems to indicate that ommochrome production dominates tryptophan metabolism at the expense of other pathways. Rather than switch metabolism in the direction of degradation when the necessary quota of ommochromes has been synthesized, it looks as though insects continue the synthesis of ommochromes which are then excreted.

Derivatives of kynurenine

Ommochromes

The discovery of the chemical nature of the ommochrome pigments and the metabolic relationship between these pigments and tryptophan followed the work begun in 1930, by Kühn, Caspari, Plagge and Ephrussi (see Ephrussi & Chevais, 1938; Caspari, 1949), who, as a result of transplantation experiments, established that certain moths (*Ephestia* and *Ptychopoda*) and the fruit-fly (*Drosophila*) had eye-colour mutants that differed from the wild type in the possession of substances which could be arranged in a unique sequence indicative of their metabolic origin.

More or less simultaneously, Becker (1939) defined the distinguishing characters of the pigments, and Tatum (1939) showed that they were derived from tryptophan. Butenandt, Weidel & Becker (1940) provided evidence that kynurenine is the immediate precursor of the pigments: if kynurenine was injected into pupae of the red-eyed mutant (*a*) of *Ephestia*, or the vermilion mutant (*v*) of *Drosophila*, adults emerged with brown coloured, wild type eyes. Kynurenine was not in fact detected in *Ephestia*, but Kikkawa (1941) isolated it from eggs of the silk-moth (*Bombyx*) and from *Drosophila* pupae. Kühn & Becker (1942) showed that there was a quantitative relationship between the amount of kynurenine injected into pupae and the amount of pigment deposited in the eyes of *Ephestia*. The now acceptable structure of kynurenine, which had previously been erroneously interpreted, was proposed by Butenandt, Weidel, Weichert & Derjugin (1943).

Danneel (1941) established that pigment formation involved the oxidation of kynurenine, and Butenandt, Weidel & Schlossberger (1949) showed that the relevant oxidation product was 3-hydroxykynurenine. With more information available about the later stages of pigment synthesis, a metabolic pathway to the ommochromes (Fig. 6) was proposed by Butenandt (1952) and Kikkawa (1953). Tryptophan is first converted to kynurenine under the influence of the wild type allele of vermilion (v) in *Drosophila*, red-eye (a) in *Ephestia*, and decolorata (dec) in *Ptychopoda*. Kynurenine is hydroxylated to 3-hydroxykynurenine under the influence of the wild type allele of cinnabar (cn) in *Drosophila*, and white eye (w^1) in *Bombyx*. Subsequent oxidation of 3-hydroxy-kynurenine probably takes place indirectly, being brought about by dopa-quinone which is reduced to dopa, the oxidation process being maintained by tyrosinase (Butenandt, Biekert & Linzen, 1956).

The ommochrome pigments have been the subject of an extensive series of publications by Butenandt and his collaborators. These include methods of extraction of the natural ommatins (Butenandt, Schiedt, Biekert & Kornmann, 1954), and an account of their distribution (Butenandt, Biekert, Kübler & Linzen, 1960). They showed that [^{14}C]tryptophan and [^{14}C]kynurenine are incorporated into the ommatins (Butenandt & Beckmann, 1955; Butenandt & Neubert, 1955). The synthesis and constitution of xanthommatin (Fig. 6) was described by Butenandt, Schiedt & Biekert (1954b) and Butenandt, Schiedt, Biekert & Cromartie (1954), and an account was given of its degradation products (Butenandt, Schiedt & Biekert, 1954a). Xanthommatin is a phenoxazone. A structure has been attributed to two other ommatins, rhodommatin (Butenandt *et al.*, 1963) a glucoside of xanthommatin, and ommatin D (Butenandt, Biekert, Koga & Traub, 1960) its sulphate ester; the structures of these are shown in Fig. 6. Ommins are substances related to ommatins, but they have a higher molecular weight and contain sulphur. Methods of isolation (Butenandt, Biekert & Linzen, 1958a) and their distribution (Butenandt, Biekert & Linzen, 1958b) have been reported; and the structure of one ommin, ommin A, has been given (Butenandt, 1960). It is a triphenoxazinethiazine (Fig. 6). Progress of the work has been summarized from time to time by Butenandt (1952, 1957, 1959, 1960).

Several other derivatives of kynurenine and 3-hydroxykynurenine have been reported, but there is at present no reason for believing that they are intermediates in ommochrome synthesis. For example, kynur-amine, the decarboxylation product of kynurenine, does not restore eye colour if injected into mutant *Drosophila* (Butenandt & Renner, 1953). Kynurine (4-hydroxyquinoline) has been reported from *Bombyx* by Butenandt, Karlson & Zillig (1951), and kynurenic acid (4-hydroxy-quinoline-2-carboxylic acid) from cinnabar eyed *Drosophila* (Danneel &

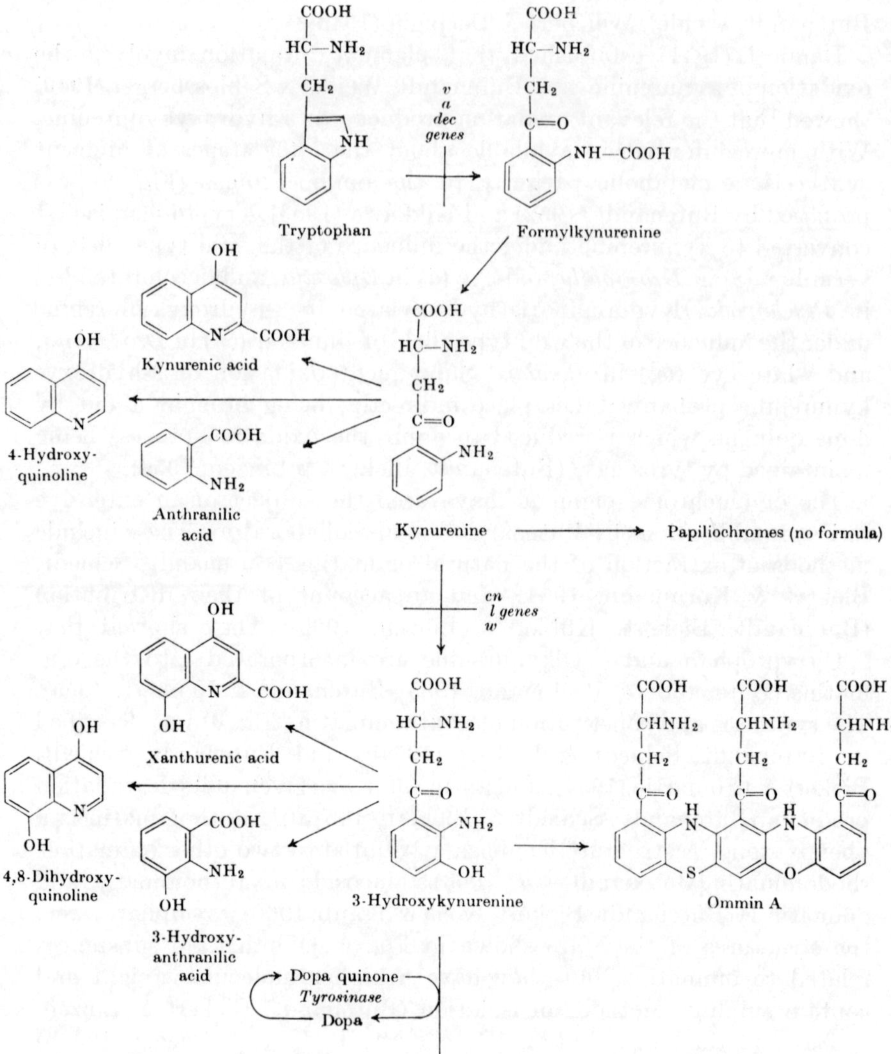

Fig. 6. The pathways of tryptophan metabolism in insects. (Mostly after Butenandt.)

Zimmermann, 1954); and 4,8-dihydroxyquinoline was also found by Butenandt *et al.* (1951) and there are several reports of xanthurenic acid (4,8-dihydroxyquinoline-2-carboxylic acid) which was found by Inagami (1955) in *Bombyx*, and Umebachi & Tsuchitani (1955) in *Drosophila*.

It is well established that the conversion of tryptophan to kynurenine takes place in two stages (Knox & Mehler, 1950; Mehler & Knox, 1950). Tryptophan peroxidase activity has however not been detected in insects despite attempts to do so by Glassman (1956) and several others cited by him, who have not published the fact. Indirect evidence is provided by the finding that vermilion mutants of *Drosophila* accumulate tryptophan, but suppressed vermilion (su^2-v) accumulate less (Green, 1949), and that formylkynurenine alleviates the deficiency brought about by the vermilion gene (Green, 1952; Kikkawa, 1953). If the wild type gene at the vermilion locus were to bring about synthesis of tryptophan peroxidase, the above findings would support this supposition. Glassman (1956) succeeded in detecting kynurenine formamidase in wild type *Drosophila*, but all the mutants that he tested had similar activity, so that this stage cannot be limiting in the production of kynurenine (and eye-pigment), again adding weight to the supposition that the vermilion gene controls synthesis of tryptophan peroxidase. 'Tryptophan pyrrolase' activity (the combined activity of the above two enzymes) has also been reported by Egelhaaf (1958) in *Ephestia*.

Kikkawa (1953) was led to believe that kynurenine was synthesized in the fat body and ovary of *Bombyx*. Rizki (1961) has substantiated this, showing that kynurenine accumulates in the fat body of wild type, but not vermilion, *Drosophila*. He has described the situation with regard to a number of isoalleles and their suppressor genes (Rizki, 1963). Later tryptophan pyrrolase activity was studied in cell-free extracts of fat body and in surviving cells, in relation to its inducibility by tryptophan and its control by vermilion and suppressor genes (Rizki & Rizki, 1963, 1964; Rizki, 1964).

No enzyme catalysing the hydroxylation of kynurenine has been described. The oxidative condensation of 3-hydroxykynurenine to xanthommatin is thought to take place at the expense of dopaquinone, involving tyrosinase (Butenandt *et al.*, 1956). Eye colour genes may affect not only the synthesis of ommochromes, but may also alter the synthesis of the chemically unrelated pteridines. It has been suggested (Forrest, 1959) that a pteridine may act as a cofactor in one of the steps leading to ommochrome formation.

The ommochromes first distinguished by Becker (1939, 1941, 1942) appear to be limited in their distribution, occurring in all arthropods that have been studied, but in only two other animals outside this phylum: in cephalopod molluscs (Schwinck, 1953) and in the eggs of an echiurid worm (Linzen, 1959b). They are mostly red, brown or violet in colour. They are characterized by their insolubility in common organic

7

solvents, and solubility in aqueous alkalis. They show redox colour change if the appropriate phenolic group is unsubstituted. Ommatins have a lower molecular weight than ommins, and the latter are generally the more stable.

The distribution of ommochromes in general is given in Linzen (1959a) and Butenandt (1959); ommatins are considered separately by Butenandt, Biekert, Kübler & Linzen (1960), and ommins by Butenandt *et al.* (1958b). Generally speaking, ommins are present (and only present) in the eyes of all insects (the cyclorrhaphous Diptera being the exception). Xanthommatin commonly accompanies ommins in eyes, and is rarely found in wings and juvenile integument. Rhodommatin and ommatin D are found in wings (particularly of vanessid butterflies) and often in remarkably large quantities in their pupal excrement. In addition, internal organs, for instance the testes (Caspari, 1933), the Malpighian tubules and the cells and lumen of the alimentary canal (Wolfram, 1949), may be coloured with ommochromes.

Characteristic changes in the pattern of pigmentation may occur, as in the case of the lime hawk moth (*Dicranura = Cerura*), and this has been shown to be associated with the rise in concentration of ecdysone in the blood that takes place before pupation. A detailed study of this process has been made by Bückmann (1952, 1959a, b, 1962; Linzen & Bückmann, 1961). A similar colour change occurs in the cuticle of the silkworm (*Bombyx*) (Kawase, 1955, 1956).

Goodwin (1950, 1952) undertook a comparison of the ommochrome content and distribution throughout the life histories of two species of locust (*Locusta* and *Schistocerca*). The amount of ommochrome increases with age, but the concentration remains fairly constant with age. The pale colour of solitary hoppers may (as in *Schistocerca*), or may not (*Locusta*), be related to total ommochrome content; in the latter case there is a depletion of the dark pigment of the cuticle. This dark pigment, often called melanin, may well be a tryptophan pigment rather than a tyrosine melanin, for when this black cuticular pigment is denatured it turns red (Pryor, 1962), which is not characteristic of a typical melanin. Certainly there is an association between ommochromes and locust 'melanin', and ommochrome granules are always present in the epidermal cells that underlie the black cuticle (Nickerson, 1956; Malek, 1957). Control of colour pattern in *Schistocerca* is under endocrine control (Nickerson, 1956). Locusts orient themselves so as to absorb the heat of the morning sun and their pigmentation must represent an important heat-exchange mechanism; it is interesting that a low breeding temperature greatly increases pigmentation (Goodwin, 1950).

Ommochromes play an obviously useful part in the life history of insects: they provide the insect with an appropriately coloured integument, and they absorb stray light in the eye, but one is struck by the consistent presence of ommochromes in situations for which there is no obvious explanation. They are often moved about the body in a predetermined way; and they are excreted in considerable amounts although they contain relatively less nitrogen than the equivalent amount of tryptophan, which at first sight would make it appear unlikely that they are simply excretory products. All this could be taken to imply that they play some unexplained but important part in, let us say, differentiation, after which they are excreted. But it must be remembered that their presence is not vital. Mutants that cannot synthesize ommochromes can survive, although they might be hard put to do so in conditions of natural competition.

Apart from their usefulness in the eye and integument, it has been suggested that they serve as respiratory pigments (Bellamy, 1958); and Pryor (1962) has pointed out that their situation in muscles and air sacs is indicative of such a function. He has also suggested that 3-hydroxy-kynurenine may be involved in the sclerotization of cuticle (Pryor, 1955), and regards the association of ommochrome pigments with sites of active sclerotization as suggestive that they are concerned in the sclerotization process (Pryor, 1962).

On the other hand it may have happened that the synthesis of ommo-chromes proved to be a character of high selective value to the insect. In order to channel tryptophan into ommochromes with the minimum loss of tryptophan into other pathways, it may have become necessary to cut off the pathway that leads by way of the anthranilic acids to ring rupture and ultimate degradation, or to nicotinic acid. As a consequence, when the necessary quota of ommochromes have been synthesized, tryptophan inexorably continues to be converted into ommochromes and this excess constitutes the unexpectedly large amount that is often found in the excreta. Consistent with this explanation is the finding that starved locusts excrete pink faeces, rich in ommochromes (Goodwin & Srisukh, 1950). If starvation were to lead to the use of bodily protein for energy provision, a rise in ommochrome excretion would be expected, the ommochromes being derived from tryptophan released from the protein.

Studies of the metabolic disorders that lead to the retention of kynurenin derivatives has provided evidence that these compounds can be carcinogenic (Boyland & Watson, 1956; Claudatus & Ginori, 1957). It would be interesting to know how the insect overcomes this problem.

Papiliochromes

The white and yellow colours of the swallowtail butterflies (Papilio-nidae) have been the subject of a study by Umebachi & Takahashi (1956). Free kynurenin appears to play a similar part in papilionids to that played by pteridines in the pierids in conferring whiteness to the wings. The yellow colours are attributable to papiliochromes, pigments that incorporate ^{14}C-tryptophan, and which yield kynurenin on degrada-tion. Very little is known about their nature, but it has been suggested (Umebachi, 1962) that they may correspond to the pigments produced as a result of interaction of kynurenin with quinones (Glassman, 1957).

The absence of nicotinic acid synthesis

It appears that nicotinic acid cannot be synthesized by any insect Schultz & Rudkin (1948) found that tryptophan had no sparing action on nicotinamide requirements of the fruit-fly (*Drosophila*). Two beetles (*Tenebrio* and *Tribolium*) have also been shown to need nicotinic acid (Fraenkel & Stern, 1951). The injection of tryptophan or quinolinic acid into *Bombyx* pupae did not lead to an increase in nicotinic acid (Ito, 1952); and anthranilic acid injected into the eggs of *Bombyx* was transformed to anthranilylglycine (Kikkawa, 1953). Anthranilic acid and anthranilylglycine occur naturally in eggs of white-1 (w^1) mutants of *Bombyx*, and the 3-hydroxy derivatives in white-2 (w^2) mutants.

It would seem that no further transformations of 3-hydroxyanthranilic acid in the direction of nicotinic acid take place. The possibility that insects channel all available tryptophan into ommochrome production has been discussed: the lack of synthesis of nicotinic acid may be a consequence of the same specialization.

Indolealkylamines

Indolealkylamines occur in insects, and 5-hydroxytryptamine has been reported from the gut, heart and Malpighian tubules (Colhoun, 1964), and from the nervous system (Gersch, Fischer, Unger & Kabitza, 1961) of the cockroach (*Periplaneta*), and of other insects (Welsh & Moorhead, 1960). Extracts of the heart (Davey, 1961) and colon (Davey, 1962) have the pharmacological activity of an indolealkylamine, and the secretion of the male sexual accessory glands of a blood-sucking bug (*Rhodnius*) and *Periplaneta* stimulates peristalsis of the oviduct by what is thought to be an o-dihydroxyindolealkylamine (Davey, 1960). 5-Hydroxytryptamine is present in insect venoms (Beard, 1963). Visceral muscle in the heart, gut and Malpighian tubules are stimulated by both 5-hydroxytryptamine and 5,6-dihydroxytryptamine, and this activity is abolished by bromolysergic acid (Colhoun, 1963a, 1964). Skeletal muscle is either unaffected (Wood, 1958), or the development of an action potential may be inhibited by indolealkylamines (Hill & Usherwood, 1961). It is thought that a peptide secretion of the corpus cardiacum stimulates an amino acid decarboxylase in the heart giving rise to the biologically active amine (Davey, 1962, 1964). Colhoun (1963b) has reported the presence of 5-hydroxytryptophan decarboxylase in the brain of *Periplaneta*.

REFERENCES

Aerts, F. E. & Vercauteren, R. E. (1964). *Enzymologia* **28**, 1.
Aerts, F., Vercauteren, R. & Decleir, R. (1960). *Proc. 11th Int. Congr. Ent., Vienna* **3**, 171.
Alexander, P. & Barton, D. H. R. (1943). *Biochem. J.* **37**, 463.

Andersen, S. O. (1963). *Biochim. biophys. Acta* **69**, 249.

Andersen, S. O. (1964). *Biochim. biophys. Acta* **93**, 213.

Andersen, S. O. & Weis-Fogh, T. (1964). *Adv. Insect Physiol.* **2**, 1.

Bailey, K. & Weis-Fogh, T. (1961). *Biochim. biophys. Acta* **48**, 452.

Beard, R. L. (1963). *A. Rev. Ent.* **8**, 1.

Becker, E. (1939). *Biol. Zbl.* **59**, 597.

Becker, E. (1941). *Naturwissenschaften* **29**, 237.

Becker, E. (1942). *Z. ind. Abst.-Vererb.* **80**, 157.

Bellamy, D. (1958). *Biochem. J.* **70**, 580.

Blaschko, H., Colhoun, E. H. & Frontali, N. (1961). *Proc. physiol. Soc.* **156**, 28.

Bodine, J. H. & Allen, T. H. (1941). *J. cell. comp. Physiol.* **18**, 151.

Boyland, E. & Watson, G. (1956). *Nature, Lond.* **177**, 837.

Bricteux-Grégoire, S., Verly, W. G. & Florkin, M. (1956). *Nature, Lond.* **177**, 1238.

Brooks, M. A. & Richards, A. G. (1955). *Biol. Bull. mar. biol. Lab., Woods Hole* **109**, 23.

Brown, B. R., Ekstrand, T., Johnson, A. W., MacDonald, S. F. & Todd, A. R. (1952). *J. chem. Soc.*, 4925.

Brown, C. H. (1950). *Nature, Lond.* **165**, 275.

Brunet, P. C. J. (1963a). *Ann. N.Y. Acad. Sci.* **100**, 1020.

Brunet, P. C. J. (1963b). *Nature, Lond.* **199**, 492.

Brunet, P. C. J. & Kent, P. W. (1955a). *Proc. R. Soc.* B **144**, 259.

Brunet, P. C. J. & Kent, P. W. (1955b). *Nature, Lond.* **175**, 819.

Bückmann, D. (1952). *Naturwissenschaften* **39**, 213.

Bückmann, D. (1959a). *J. Insect Physiol.* **3**, 159.

Bückmann, D. (1959b). *Verh. dt. zool. Ges., Frankfurt*, 137.

Bückmann, D. (1962). *Verh. dt. zool. Ges., Wien*, 180.

Butenandt, A. (1952). *Endeavour* **11**, 188.

Butenandt, A. (1957). *Angew. Chem.* **69**, 16.

Butenandt, A. (1959). *Naturwissenschaften* **46**, 461.

Butenandt, A. (1960). *Proc. 17th Int. Congr. pure appl. Chem., Munich* **2**, 11.

Butenandt, A. & Beckmann, R. (1955). *Hoppe-Seyler's Z. physiol. Chem.* **301**, 116.

Butenandt, A., Biekert, E., Koga, N. & Traub, P. (1960). *Hoppe-Seyler's Z. physiol. Chem.* **321**, 258.

Butenandt, A., Biekert, E., Kübler, H. & Linzen, B. (1960). *Hoppe-Seyler's Z. physiol. Chem.*, **319**, 238.

Butenandt, A., Biekert, E., Kübler, H., Linzen, B. & Traub, P. (1963). *Hoppe-Seyler's Z. physiol. Chem.* **334**, 71.

Butenandt, A., Biekert, E. & Linzen, B. (1956). *Hoppe-Seyler's Z. physiol. Chem.* **305**, 284.

Butenandt, A., Biekert, E. & Linzen, B. (1958a). *Hoppe-Seyler's Z. physiol. Chem.* **312**, 227.

Butenandt, A., Biekert, E. & Linzen, B. (1958b). *Hoppe-Seyler's Z. physiol. Chem.* **313**, 251.

Butenandt, A., Karlson, P. & Zillig, W. (1951). *Hoppe-Seyler's Z. physiol. Chem.* **288**, 125.

Butenandt, A. & Neubert, G. (1955). *Hoppe-Seyler's Z. physiol. Chem.* **301**, 109.

Butenandt, A. & Renner, U. (1953). *Z. Naturf.* **8b**, 454.

Butenandt, A., Schiedt, U. & Biekert, E. (1954a). *Justus Liebigs Annln Chem.* **586**, 229.

Butenandt, A., Schiedt, U. & Biekert, E. (1954b). *Justus Liebigs Annln Chem.* **588**, 106.

Butenandt, A., Schiedt, U., Biekert, E. & Cromartie, R. J. T. (1954). *Justus Liebigs Annln Chem.* **590**, 75.

Butenandt, A., Schiedt, U., Biekert, E. & Kornmann, P. (1954). *Justus Liebigs Annln Chem.* **586**, 217.

Butenandt, A., Weidel, W. & Becker, E. (1940). *Naturwissenschaften* **28**, 63.

Butenandt, A., Weidel, W. & Schlossberger, H. (1949). *Z. Naturf.* **4b**, 242.

Butenandt, A., Weidel, W., Weichert, R. & Derjugin, W. von (1943). *Hoppe-Seyler's Z. physiol. Chem.* **279**, 27.

Campbell, F. L. (1929). *Ann. ent. Soc. Am.* **22**, 401.

Caspari, E. (1933). *Arch. EntwMech. Org.* **130**, 253.

Caspari, E. (1949). *Q. Rev. Biol.* **24**, 185.

Chen, P. S. (1962). In *Amino Acid Pools*, Ed. Holden, J. T. London: Elsevier.
Claudatus, J. & Ginori, S. (1957). *Science* **125**, 394.
Colhoun, E. H. (1963a). *Adv. Insect Physiol.* **1**, 1.
Colhoun, E. H. (1963b). *Experientia* **19**, 9.
Colhoun, E. H. (1964). In *Comparative Neurochemistry*, Ed. Richter, D. Oxford: Pergamon.
Cottrell, C. B. (1964). *Adv. Insect Physiol.* **2**, 175.
Dalgliesh, C. E. & Tabechian, H. (1956). *Biochem. J.* **62**, 625.
Danneel, R. (1941). *Biol. Zbl.* **61**, 388.
Danneel, R. & Zimmermann, B. (1954). *Z. Naturf.* **9b**, 788.
Davey, K. G. (1960). *Can. J. Zool.* **38**, 39.
Davey, K. G. (1961). *Nature, Lond.* **192**, 284.
Davey, K. G. (1962). *J. exp. Biol.* **39**, 319.
Davey, K. G. (1964). *Adv. Insect Physiol.* **2**, 219.
Davies, J. B. (1964). Thesis, University of Oxford.
Dennell, R. (1956). *Nature, Lond.* **178**, 922.
Dennell, R. (1958). *Biol. Rev.* **33**, 178.
Dresse, A., Jeniaux, C. & Florkin, M. (1960). *Archs int. Physiol. Biochim.* **68**, 196.
Duchâteau, G. & Florkin, M. (1958). *Archs int. Physiol. Biochim.* **66**, 573.
Dutton, G. J. (1962). *Comp. Biochem. Physiol.* **7**, 39.
Dutton, G. J. & Duncan, A. M. (1960). *Biochem. J.* **77**, 18P.
Egelhaaf, A. (1958). *Z. Naturf.* **13b**, 275.
Ephrussi, B. & Chevais, S. (1938). *Bull. biol. Fr. Belg.* **72**, 48.
Florkin, M. & Jeniaux, C. (1964). In *Physiology of Insecta*, Vol. 3, Ed. Rockstein, M. New York: Academic Press.
Ford, E. B. (1941). *Proc. R. ent. Soc. Lond.* B **16**, 65.
Forrest, H. S. (1959). In *Pigment Cell Biology*, Ed. Gordon, M. New York: Academic Press.
Fraenkel, G. & Rudall, K. M. (1947). *Proc. R. Soc.* B **134**, 111.
Fraenkel, G. & Stern, A. R. (1951). *Arch. Biochem.* **30**, 438.
Fukuda, T. (1956). *J. Biochem., Tokyo* **43**, 137.
Furneaux, P. J. S. & McFarlane, J. E. (1965). *J. Insect. Physiol.* **11**, 591.
Fuzeau-Braesch, S. (1960). *Bull. biol. Fr. Belg.* **94**, 525.
Gersch, M., Fischer, F., Unger, H. & Kabitza, W. (1961). *Z. Naturf.* **16b**, 351.
Gilmour, D. (1961). *The Biochemistry of Insects*. London: Academic Press.
Gilmour, D. (1965). *The Metabolism of Insects*. London: Oliver & Boyd.
Glassman, E. (1956). *Genetics* **41**, 566.
Glassman, E. (1957). *Arch. Biochem. Biophys.* **67**, 74.
Goodwin, T. W. (1950). *Biochem. J.* **47**, 554.
Goodwin, T. W. (1952). *Biol. Rev.* **27**, 439.
Goodwin, T. W. & Srisukh, S. (1950). *Biochem. J.* **47**, 549.
Green, M. M. (1949). *Genetics* **34**, 564.
Green, M. M. (1952). *Proc. natn. Acad. Sci. U.S.A.* **38**, 300.
Gustavson, K. H. (1949). *Adv. Protein Chem.* **5**, 353.
Gustavson, K. H. (1956). *The Chemistry of Tanning Processes*. New York: Academic Press.
Hackman, R. H. (1953a). *Biochem. J.* **54**, 362.
Hackamn, R. H. (1953b). *Biochem. J.* **54**, 367.
Hackman, R. H. (1953c). *Biochem. J.* **54**, 371.
Hackman, R. H. (1964). In *The Physiology of Insecta*, Vol. 3, Ed. Rockstein, M. New York: Academic Press.
Hackman, R. H. & Goldberg, M. (1958). *J. Insect Physiol.* **2**, 221.
Hackman, R. H. & Goldberg, M. (1963). *Biochim. biophys. Acta* **71**, 738.
Hackman, R. H., Pryor, M. G. M. & Todd, A. R. (1948). *Biochem. J.* **43**, 474.
Hackman, R. H. & Todd, A. R. (1953). *Biochem. J.* **55**, 631.
Harley-Mason, J. (1960). *Proc. 17th Int. Congr. pure appl. Chem., Munich*, **2**, 35.

Henderson, L. H., Gholson, R. K. & Dalgliesh, C. E. (1962). In *Comparative Biochemistry*, Vol. 4, Eds. Florkin, M. & Mason, H. S. New York: Academic Press.

Henry, S. M. (1962). *Trans. N.Y. Acad. Sci.* **24**, 676.

Hill, R. B. & Usherwood, P. N. R. (1961). *J. Physiol.* **157**, 393.

Horowitz, N. H. & Fling, M. (1955). In *Amino Acid Metabolism*, Eds. McElroy, W. D. & Glass, H. B. Baltimore: Johns Hopkins.

Imaizumi, R., Yoshida, H. & Kita, T. (1958). *Jap. J. Pharmac.* **8**, 9.

Inagami, K. (1955). *J. seric. Sci., Tokyo* **24**, 295.

Ito, T. (1952). *Jap. J. Genet.* **27**, 75.

Karlson, P. (1959). *Proc. 4th Int. Congr. Biochem., Vienna* **12**, 37.

Karlson, P. (1960). *Hoppe-Seyler's Z. physiol. Chem.* **318**, 194.

Karlson, P. (1962a). *Proc. 8th Symp. dt. Ges. Endocr. Munich*, 90.

Karlson, P. (1962b). *Gen. comp. Endocr. Suppl.* **1**, 1.

Karlson, P. & Ammon, H. (1963). *Hoppe-Seyler's Z. physiol. Chem.* **330**, 161.

Karlson, P. & Herrlich, P. (1965). *J. Insect Physiol.* **11**, 79.

Karlson, P. & Hoffmeister, H. (1961). *Scientia* **55**, 344.

Karlson, P. & Liebau, H. (1961). *Hoppe-Seyler's Z. physiol. Chem.* **326**, 135.

Karlson, P., Mergenhagen, D. & Sekeris, C. E. (1964). *Hoppe-Seyler's Z. physiol. Chem.* **338**, 42.

Karlson, P. & Schlossberger-Raecke, I. (1962). *J. Insect Physiol.* **8**, 441.

Karlson, P. & Schweiger, A. (1961). *Hoppe-Seyler's Z. physiol. Chem.* **323**, 199.

Karlson, P. & Sekeris, C. E. (1962a). *Biochim. biophys. Acta* **63**, 489.

Karlson, P. & Sekeris, C. E. (1962b). *Nature, Lond.* **195**, 183.

Karlson, P., Sekeris, C. E. & Herrlich, P. (1963). *Dt. med. Wschr.* **88**, 1873.

Karlson, P., Sekeris, C. E. & Sekeri, K. E. (1962). *Hoppe-Seyler's Z. physiol. Chem.* **327**, 86.

Kasting, R. & McGinnis, A. J. (1958). *Nature, Lond.* **182**, 1380.

Kasting, R. & McGinnis, A. J. (1962). *J. Insect Physiol.* **8**, 97.

Kawase, S. (1955). *J. seric. Sci., Tokyo* **24**, 353.

Kawase, S. (1956). *J. seric. Sci., Tokyo* **25**, 295.

Kawase, S. (1958). *Nature, Lond.* **181**, 1350.

Kennaugh, J. H. (1958). *J. Insect Physiol.* **2**, 97.

Kent, P. W. & Brunet, P. C. J. (1959). *Tetrahedron* **7**, 252.

Kettlewell, H. B. D. (1958). *Proc. 10th Int. Congr. Ent., Montreal* **2**, 831.

Kikkawa, H. (1941). *Genetics* **26**, 587.

Kikkawa, H. (1953). *Adv. Genet.* **5**, 107.

Knox, W. E. & Mehler, A. H. (1950). *J. biol. Chem.* **187**,419.

Kühn, A. & Becker, E. (1942). *Biol. Zbl.* **62**, 303.

Lewis, H. W. (1962). *Biol. Bull. mar. biol. Lab., Woods Hole* **123**, 464.

Linzen, B. (1959a). *Verh. dt. zool. Ges., Frankfurt*, 154.

Linzen, B. (1959b). *Hoppe-Seyler's Z. physiol. Chem.* **314**, 12.

Linzen, B. & Bückmann, D. (1961). *Z. Naturf.* **16b**, 6.

Lipke, H. & Fraenkel, G. (1956). *A. Rev. Ent.* **1**, 17.

Malek, S. R. A. (1957). *Nature, Lond.* **180**, 237.

Malek, S. R. A. (1961). *Comp. Biochem. Physiol.* **2**, 35.

Mason, H. S. (1955a). *Nature, Lond.* **175**, 771.

Mason, H. S. (1955b). *Adv. Enzymol.* **16**, 105.

Mason, H. S. (1959). In *Pigment Cell Biology*, Ed. Gordon, M. New York: Academic Press.

Mason, H. S., Fowlks, W. L. & Peterson, E. (1955). *J. Am. chem. Soc.* **77**, 2914.

Mason, H. S. & Peterson, E. W. (1955). *J. biol. Chem.* **212**, 485.

Mehler, A. H. & Knox, W. E. (1950). *J. biol. Chem.* **187**, 431.

Mergenhagen, D. (1964). *Hoppe-Seyler's Z. physiol. Chem.* **338**, 113.

Mitchell, H. K., Chen, P. S. & Hadorn, E. (1960). *Experientia* **16**, 410.

Moore, B. P. (1964). *Austr. J. Chem.* **17**, 901.

Myers, C. M. & Smith, J. N. (1954). *Biochem. J.* **56**, 498.

Nickerson, B. (1956). *Anti-Locust Bull.* No. 24.

Ohnishi, E. (1953). *Jap. J. Zool.* **11**, 69.

Ohnishi, E. (1954a). *Annotnes zool. jap.* **27**, 76.

Ohnishi, E. (1954b). *Annotnes zool. jap.* **27**, 188.

Ohnishi, E. (1958). *Jap. J. Zool.* **12**, 179.

Ohnishi, E. (1959). *J. Insect Physiol.* **3**, 219.

Okubo, S. (1958). *Med. J. Osaka Univ.* **9**, 327.

Östlund, E. (1954). *Acta physiol. scand.* **31**, 1.

Pavan, M. (1959). *Proc. 4th Int. Congr. Biochem.*, Vienna **12**, 15.

Pryor, M. G. M. (1940a). *Proc. R. Soc.* B **128**, 378.

Pryor, M. G. M. (1940b). *Proc. R. Soc.* B **128**, 393.

Pryor, M. G. M. (1955). *Nature, Lond.* **175**, 600.

Pryor, M. G. M. (1962). In *Comparative Biochemistry*, Vol. 4, Ed. Florkin, M. & Mason, H. S. New York: Academic Press.

Pryor, M. G. M., Russell, P. B. & Todd, A. R. (1946). *Biochem. J.* **40**, 627.

Pryor, M. G. M., Russell, P. B. & Todd, A. R. (1947). *Nature, Lond.* **159**, 399.

Quilico, A., Piozzi, F., Pavan, M. & Mantica, E. (1959). *Tetrahedron* **5**, 10.

Raper, H. S. (1928). *Physiol. Rev.* **8**, 245.

Richards, A. G. & Brooks, M. A. (1958). *A. Rev. Ent.* **3**, 37.

Rizki, T. M. (1961). *J. biophys. biochem. Cytol.* **9**, 567.

Rizki, T. M. (1963). *J. Cell Biol.* **16**, 573.

Rizki, T. M. (1964). *J. Cell Biol.* **21**, 203.

Rizki, T. M. & Rizki, R. M. (1963). *J. Cell Biol.* **17**, 87.

Rizki, T. M. & Rizki, R. M. (1964). *J. Cell Biol.* **21**, 27.

Roth, L. M. & Stay, B. (1958). *J. Insect Physiol.* **1**, 305.

Sapag-Hagar, M., González-González, M. P. & Stamm-Menéndez, M. D. (1961). *Revta esp. Fisiol.* **17**, 89.

Schildknecht, H. (1957). *Angew. Chem.* **69**, 62.

Schmalfuss, H. (1937). *Biochem. Z.* **294**, 112.

Schmalfuss, H. & Barthmeyer, H. (1930). *Z. ind. Abst.-Vererb.* **53**, 67.

Schmalfuss, H. & Barthmeyer, H. (1931). *Z. ind. Abst.-Vererb.* **58**, 332.

Schmalfuss, H., Heider, A. & Winklemann, K. (1933). *Biochem. Z.* **257**, 188.

Schultz, J. & Rudkin, G. T. (1948). *Fedn Proc. Fedn Am. Socs exp. Biol.* **7**, 1850.

Schweiger, A. & Karlson, P. (1962). *Hoppe-Seyler's Z. physiol. Chem.* **329**, 210.

Schwinck, I. (1953). *Naturwissenschaften* **40**, 365.

Sekeris, C. E. (1963a). *Hoppe-Seyler's Z. physiol. Chem.* **332**, 70.

Sekeris, C. E. (1963b). In *Radiation and Radioisotopes applied to Insects of Agricultural Importance.* Vienna: International Atomic Energy Agency.

Sekeris, C. R. (1964). *Science* **144**, 419.

Sekeris, C. E. & Karlson, P. (1962). *Biochim. biophys. Acta* **62**, 103.

Sekeris, C. E. & Mergenhagen, D. (1964). *Science* **145**, 68.

Smith, J. N. (1962). *A. Rev. Ent.* **7**, 465.

Smith, J. N. & Turbert, H. (1961). *Nature, Lond.* **189**, 600.

Stay, B. & Roth, L. M. (1962). *Ann. ent. Soc. Am.* **55**, 124.

Tatum, E. L. (1939). *Proc. natn. Acad. Sci. U.S.A.* **25**, 486.

Thomson, R. H. (1957). *Naturally Occurring Quinones.* London: Butterworth.

Thompson, D. L. (1926). *Biochem. J.* **20**, 73.

Tomino, S. (1965). *J. Insect. Physiol.* **11**, 581.

Trim, A. R. (1941). *Biochem. J.* **35**, 1088.

Trivelloni, J. C. (1960). *Arch. Biochem. Biophys.* **89**, 149.

Umebachi, Y. (1962). *Sci. Rep. Kanazawa Univ.* **8**, 135.

Umebachi, Y. & Takahashi, H. (1956). *J. Biochem., Tokyo* **43**, 73.

Umebachi, Y. & Tsuchitani, K. (1955). *J. Biochem., Tokyo* **42**, 817.

Vercauteren, R., Aerts, R. & Decleir, F. (1960). *Proc. 11th Int. Congr. Ent.*, Vienna **3**, 167.

Waddington, C. H. (1941). *Proc. zool. Soc. Lond.* A **111**, 173.

Weis-Fogh, T. (1960). *J. exp. Biol.* **37**, 889.

Weis-Fogh, T. (1961a). *J. molec. Biol.* **3**, 520.

Weis-Fogh, T. (1961b). *J. molec. Biol.* **3**, 648.

Welsh, J. H. & Moorhead, M. (1960). *J. Neurochem.* **6**, 146.

Whitehead, D. L., Brunet, P. C. J. & Kent, P. W. (1960). *Nature, Lond.* **185**, 610.

Wigglesworth, V. B. (1964). *Adv. Insect Physiol.* **2**, 247.

Wolfram, R. (1949). *Z. ind. Abst.-Vererb.* **83**, 254.

Wood, D. W. (1958). *J. exp. Biol.* **35**, 850.

Yasonobu, K. T. (1959). In *Pigment Cell Biology*, Ed. Gordon, M. New York: Academic Press.

HORMONES CONTROLLING GROWTH AND DEVELOPMENT IN INSECTS

By V. B. WIGGLESWORTH

Department of Zoology, University of Cambridge, England

THE centre of the endocrine system of the insect consists of neuro-secretory cells in the brain. The axons from these cells carry neuro-secretory granules to the 'corpus cardiacum' where the *brain hormone* is liberated into the blood. The brain hormone activates a second endocrine organ, the 'thoracic gland', and causes this to secrete the *moulting hormone* (ecdysone) which acts directly upon the growing tissues. A third endocrine organ, lying just behind the corpus cardiacum, is the 'corpus allatum'; throughout the young stages of the insect the corpus allatum secretes the *juvenile hormone* (neotenine).

When the epidermal cells are exposed to the moulting hormone in the presence of the juvenile hormone they separate from the cuticle, grow, and lay down a new cuticle of larval type. When the larva is fully grown, the corpus allatum no longer secretes the juvenile hormone; the moulting hormone acts alone. Moulting occurs as before, but the new cuticle is now of adult type.

THE MODE OF ACTION OF THE GROWTH HORMONES

(i) It is shown both histologically and experimentally that the *brain hormone* activates the thoracic gland. It is possible that the neuro-secretory product serves as raw material for hormone production.

(ii) Between moults the epidermal cells are dormant and inactive, with small nucleoli, little cytoplasm and few mitochondria. They are activated by the *moulting hormone*, ecdysone; the nucleolus enlarges, ribonucleoprotein accumulates in the cytoplasm, and the mitochondria increase. This renewed protein synthesis leads to cell division and cuticle formation. Attempts have been made to identify synthesis of cyto-chrome *c*, or nucleoprotein synthesis, or, most recently, DNA synthesis, as the primary effect of ecdysone—but all these processes are conse-quences of the termination of dormancy.

The giant chromosomes in the salivary glands of *Chironomus* or *Drosophila* larvae, within half an hour of exposure to ecdysone, show enlargement of certain gene loci to form 'puffs'. Specific parts of the gene system are being activated. It is inferred from these observations

79

that the primary site of action of the hormone may be certain gene loci which lead to the production of organ-specific enzyme systems. According to this hypothesis the biochemical results of the action of the moulting hormone will vary from one type of cell to another. That is well known to be true.

(iii) The insect has a gene system in part responsible for larval characters, and in part responsible for adult characters. The *juvenile hormone* is a morphogenetic hormone which brings into operation those components of the gene system responsible for the development of larval characters throughout the body, with the simultaneous suppression of adult characters. The precise mechanism of this genetic switch is not known. Here again the biochemical results will vary from one part of the body to another.

THE CHEMISTRY OF THE GROWTH HORMONES

(i) According to one group of workers the *brain hormone* from the silkworm pupa is contained in an oily extract from the brain, and the active principle is claimed to be cholesterol. Another group has claimed that the active principle is a peptide hormone present in saline extracts of the brain.

(ii) The moulting hormone, *ecdysone*, has been isolated in crystalline form from pupae of the blowfly and of the silkworm. It has a molecular weight of 464, an empirical formula $C_{27}H_{44}O_6$. It appears to be a steroid but the complete chemical formula is not known. Indeed some five separate types of ecdysone have been separated by counter current partition. The injection of isotopically labelled cholesterol in the blowfly pupa leads to the production of labelled ecdysone.

(iii) The *juvenile hormone* is present in relatively large amounts in ether extracts of the cecropia silkmoth of North America. Methods of biological assay based on this material have been used to demonstrate that substances with the same activity are widely distributed, not only in insects, but in other invertebrates, in mammals including man, and in some higher plants, yeasts and bacteria.

The active principle as found in the excreta of the mealworm *Tenebrio*, and also in yeast, has proved to be a mixture of *trans-trans*-farnesol and farnesal. This material will reproduce in insects all the biological effects of the juvenile hormone. Farnesol (at least in the beetle *Tenebrio* and the bug *Rhodnius*) is more effective if the C-1 end of the molecule is blocked, as in the methyl or ethyl ether, or in farnesyl acetone. But even this material is completely inactive if it is injected in emulsified form; and the water-soluble farnesyl pyrophosphate is also inactive; as are geraniol, nerolidol, phytol, squalene, etc. Maximum activity is obtained if the farnesyl methyl ether is injected in dilute solution (0·1–1·0%) in olive oil. The material is apparently taken up by the blood cells and liberated in an active form. Less than 5 μg injected in this way will reproduce all the effects of an implanted corpus allatum in a *Rhodnius* larva weighing 200 mg.—and, of course, the quantity of the active substance actually utilized must be far less than this.

Whether the natural juvenile hormone is a derivative, or complex, of farnesol is still *sub judice*. It has been shown by Schmialek that the extract from cecropia contains farnesol and farnesal; and that labelled mevalonic acid injected into cecropia is converted into farnesol, farnesal and nerolidol. The American workers (Schneiderman, Gilbert *et al.*) while agreeing that farnesol is present in cecropia extracts, maintain that the active principle is certainly not farnesol, though its identity is not known. A. N. Clements, in a preliminary communication to the International Congress of Entomology last year, reported that the labelled fraction isolated from cecropia after injection of labelled mevalonic acid would not volatilize at any temperature in the gas chromatography column.

As a provisional hypothesis it may be suggested that the active substance, or 'prosthetic group', is indeed the triple isoprene unit of *trans-trans*-farnesol; but that this is tied to some carrier, perhaps of a lipoprotein nature, in which combination it is more stable and physiological in its action than free farnesol.

REFERENCE

Wigglesworth, V. B. (1964). The hormonal regulation of growth and reproduction in insects. *Adv. Insect Physiol.* **2**, 244–332.

ADDENDUM

Bibliography of recent biochemical work on insect hormones

Burdette, W. C. & Bullock, M. W. (1963). Ecdysone: five biologically active fractions from *Bombyx*. *Science* **140**, 1311.
Butenandt, A. & Karlson, P. (1954). Über die Isolierung eines Metamorphose-Hormons der Insekten in kristallisierter Form. *Z. Naturf.* **9b**, 389–391.
Ichikawa, M. & Ishizaki, H. (1963). Protein nature of the brain hormone of insects. *Nature, Lond.* **198**, 308–309.
Karlson, P. & Hoffmeister, H. (1963). Zur Biogenese des Ecdysons. i. Umwandlung von Cholesterin in Ecdyson. *Hoppe-Seyler's Z. physiol. Chem.* **331**, 298–300.
Karlson, P., Hoffmeister, H., Hoppe, W. & Huber, R. (1963). Zur Chemie des Ecdysons. *Justus Liebigs Annln Chem.* **662**, 1–20.
Kirimura, J., Saito, M. & Kobayashi, M. (1962). Steroid hormone in an insect *Bombyx mori*. *Nature, Lond.* **195**, 729–730.
Meyer, A. S., Schneiderman, H. A. & Gilbert, L. I. (1965). A highly purified preparation of juvenile hormone from the silk moth *Hyalophora cecropia* L. *Nature, Lond.* **206**, 272–275.
Schmialek, P. (1961). Die Identifizierung zweier im Tenebriokot und in Hefe vorkommender Substanzen mit Juvenilhormonewirkung. *Z. Naturf.* **16b**, 461–464.
Schmialek, P. (1963a). Über die Bildung von Juvenilhormonen in Wildseidenspinnern. *Z. Naturf.* **18b**, 462–465.
Schmialek, P. (1963b). Metamorphosehemmung von *Tenebrio molitor* durch Farnesylmethyläther. *Z. Naturf.* **18b**, 513–515.

Schmialek, P. (1963c). Über Verbindungen mit Juvenilhormonwirkung. *Z. Naturf.* **18b**, 516–519.

Schneiderman, H. A. & Gilbert, L. I. (1964). Control of growth and development in insects. *Science* **143**, 325–333.

Wigglesworth, V. B. (1963a). The juvenile hormone effect of farnesol and some related compounds: quantitative experiments. *J. Insect Physiol.* **9**, 105–119.

Wigglesworth, V. B. (1964). The hormonal regulation of growth and reproduction in insects. *Adv. Insect Physiol.* **2**, 244–332.

SKELETAL STRUCTURE IN INSECTS

By K. M. RUDALL

Astbury Department of Biophysics, The University, Leeds, England

WHERE we find solid extracellular protective or skeletal substances there is generally a complex system of fibrous molecules and these lend themselves to study by physical means such as X-ray analysis. Indeed this may be a very good way of beginning to study the problems involved because the material may be relatively insoluble without using drastic procedures that could degrade the molecular structure and thus prevent the detection of well-defined molecular species or macromolecular systems. While the physical investigations can be a superlative guide with such materials, they form only part of the complete information we require and much of this lies in the biochemical field.

The secrets in the solid extracellular substances of insects are of interest in themselves, but they are also related to those of macromolecular structures occurring widely in animal tissues. For example, in studying the chitin/protein complexes of insect cuticles we are dealing with a polysaccharide of N-acetylglucosamine which is related to the important hexosamine-containing polysaccharides of vertebrate tissue. However, when viewed in one way, the chitin/protein skeleton of insects is the reverse of the collagenous skeleton in vertebrates. In the former we have as a model a polysaccharide fibrous framework (chitin) reinforced and modified by less obviously fibrous protein, while in the latter we have a protein fibrous framework (collagen) reinforced and modified by a polysaccharide matrix. The wider importance of studies on silk proteins is that we have among them the whole range of chain conformations recognized in fibrous proteins anywhere, and with the interesting conclusion that the collagen type of protein is most closely related to the classical fibroin structures (Rudall, 1962).

CHITIN/PROTEIN SYSTEMS IN INSECT CUTICLE

Thinking in terms of macromolecular structure several different types of chitin-protein assembly are recognized by X-ray means (Rudall, 1963). Two of these are comparatively well defined and of interesting distribution. The first system is that of soft mobile cuticles, the same characteristic structure being found in all dipteran and lepidopteran larvae examined, as well as in the larval cuticle of the beetle *Geotrupes*.

It has also been found in adult intersegmental membranes of lobster and praying mantis. The molecular structure having these features is judged to be one giving the appropriate plasticity and flexibility. The properties of cuticles are also modified by discrete layers of protein alone, such as in those special cases where there are separate layers of 'resilin', an elastin-like protein described by Weis-Fogh and colleagues (Andersen & Weis-Fogh, 1964). In the present cases, by contrast, we are looking at the still more intimate association of chitin and protein, a protein which is co-valently linked to chitin chains or is closely investing small groups of chitin chains.

The second chitin/protein system of interest occurs in the hard, non-plastic cuticle of some adult insects. This system is found in its best defined form in the hardened cuticle of all Hymenopterans so far examined. One distinct modification of this system occurs in true Orthoptera (grasshoppers, locusts, crickets) while yet another is charac-teristic of the chaetae of the Annelid, *Aphrodite*. This wide occurrence indicates its importance in any attempt to reach an understanding of chitin/protein complexes. The long ovipositors of Hymenoptera are favourable material for investigating the structure in more detail and we give some results of a study of Ichneumons, such as species of Rhyssa. Fig. 1 is an X-ray diffraction photograph of the ovipositor of *Megar-hyssa nortoni nortoni*, to be compared with purified fibrous chitin, Fig. 2, where the protein and other non-chitin constituents have been removed. Fig. 1 is remarkable for the well developed series of meridional reflections based on a fundamental axial period of 31 Å, ten of these orders being easily visible. The strong 3rd, 6th and 9th layer lines correspond with the structure of the chitin framework which is seen by itself in Fig. 2. In Fig. 2 the chitin chains have aggregated into relatively large crystalline arrays and by comparison with this, Fig. 1 is consistent with a picture for natural intact cuticle of small groups of chitin chains separated by thin 'layers' of protein such that 'the chitin group plus the protein layer' forms the basic unit of a definable chitin/protein complex.

By recording the wider angle 'reflections' with a cylindrical camera up to 33 orders of the 31 Å period have been observed. Between each of the axial orders of the true chitin spectrum (Fig. 2) there are two additional evenly spaced reflections in the case of the natural intact structure as is readily seen in Fig. 1. Thus every third subperiod of the 31 Å repeating structure *exactly* corresponds with those of the chitin structure. This suggests that some macromolecule repeating along the fibre axis at 31 Å is specifically associated with chitin to form a special macromolecular system. This macromolecule, so intimately associated with chitin, is thought to be protein because that is the only substance known to be present in cuticles in large quantities. In this material the structure giving periodicity of 31 Å is stabilized by the dark brown tanning process and it is removed by hot dilute caustic alkali. Evans (1938) gives some figures for the constitution of wasp abdominal cuticle which has a similar

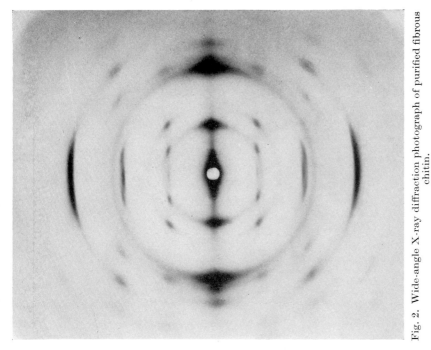

Fig. 2. Wide-angle X-ray diffraction photograph of purified fibrous chitin.

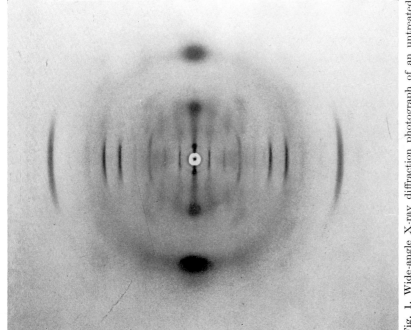

Fig. 1. Wide-angle X-ray diffraction photograph of an untreated intact Ichneumon ovipositor (*Megarhyssa*).

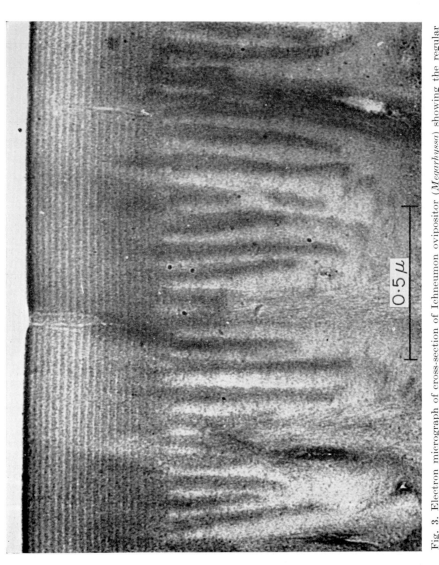

0.5 μ

Fig. 3. Electron micrograph of cross-section of Ichneumon ovipositor (*Megarhyssa*) showing the regular layered structure of the outer regions of the wall.

molecular structure to that of the ovipositors described here. Although Evans's studies were carried out using insufficiently long periods of extraction and in too weak a solution of alkali to reach constancy of residue weight, his results are consistent with a constitution of some 25% chitin while the remainder of the cuticle is essentially pigment/protein. A search is being made to see if we can eliminate macromolecules other than protein as being responsible for the macroperiod observed. At least we can say that it is unlikely to be lipids as boiling for 40 hr in benzene has no effect.

If it is protein that gives rise to the 31 Å structure can we recognize any of the known conformations of fibrous proteins in it? The presence of this prominent structure in Hymenopteran cuticles has been known for a long time (Picken & Lotmar, 1950) and subperiods of 31 Å were seen to be of interest as they corresponded exactly or closely with those of the principal natural fibrous molecules then known. A more complete list of correspondences is given in Table 1.

Table 1. *Orders of 31Å which correspond with principal axial spacings in the various types of fibrous protein*

Order of 31 Å	5th	6th	9th	10th	11th	21st	27th	28th	31st	32nd
d in Å	6·2	5·16	3·44	3·1	2·82	1·48	1·15	1·11	1·0	0·97
Fibrous protein type	Feather keratin	α-Keratin	β-Keratin	Feather keratin	Collagen	α-Helix	Silk fibroin	β-Keratin	γ-Helix	

It seemed possible to entertain the view that just as the 31 Å structure is associated with chains of chitin, it might equally become associated with the other fibrous structures, feather keratin, α-keratin, β-keratin, collagen, etc. If this were so, it could be looked upon as a 'master protein' playing an important part in the organization of intracellular and extracellular fibres.

But it is our present concern to see if there are any unusual intensities in the axial subperiods of the 31 Å system which might suggest its closer relationship with just one of the known protein structures. Of the subperiods listed in Table 1, all of which are observed, the only ones having specially high intensity are the 5th and 10th orders, i.e. the reflections at 6·2 Å and 3·1 Å. So there is the suggestion that the structure could be related to the feather keratin type of protein. The lack of special intensity at 1·5, 1·15 or 1·11 Å does not suggest that there is an oriented system of α or β protein chains.

Having discovered these systems in insect cuticles by X-ray studies, it is clear that electron microscopy should be able to deny or support the general nature of the structure which is proposed, and also provide additional information. Fig. 1 shows very well defined reflections on the equator with a spacing of 35 Å, which, incidentally, is comparable with

8

that on the equator in diffraction photographs of soft larval cuticles and adult intersegmental membranes (Rudall, 1963) though it may have a very different origin. In Fig. 1 also, the first axial reflection at 31 Å clearly consists of two off-axis spots suggesting a larger fundamental repeat than 35 Å at right angles to the fibre axis. Electron micrographs by Mr. A. Millard of cross-sections of ovipositors, show two main fine structures. Superficially there is a $0.5\ \mu$ thick system of layers (Fig. 3) which we might associate with the special 'hardness' or 'toughness' required at the surface of this wood boring instrument. The individual layers are very regular, about 250 Å thick and with a number of sub-divisions. But, apart from these layers, some pore canals and tongue-like processes, the bulk of the ovipositor wall appears in cross-section as in Fig. 4, consisting of regular non-staining cores (chitin) surrounded by thin uniform layers of highly staining material which we interpret as the protein. In places these rods are in regular hexagonal array. High resolution X-ray photographs give a strong reflection at 63 Å in addition to the moderately intense reflection at 35·3 Å, these spacings being related as $\sqrt{3}:1$. Measurement of the electron micrographs gives $a/2$, of the hexagonal array, as about 40 Å. Thus it can be said that the low angle diffraction pattern originates from the hexagonally packed system of chitin rods separated by protein. Longitudinal sections parallel to the lengths of the rods should give clues as to the meaning of the 31 Å axial periodicity.

These beginnings of successful electron microscope studies on chitin/protein systems support the experience of X-ray work that there is a macromolecular unit of chitin plus protein. Considering the dimensions in Fig. 4 we give an approximate constitution in these regions of 35% chitin. Granting greater concentration of protein in other regions and we note the heavier staining with uranyl acetate at the peripheral regions of Fig. 3 and in the processes descending down from them, the total chitin content of such a sample of cuticle may be significantly lower than 35%. X-ray studies of a wide range of chitinous cuticles (Rudall, 1963) have indicated the existence of a number of different associations of protein with chitin. The variation of geometry in Fig. 3 indicates that cuticular structures can contain side by side different chitin/protein complexes with one type predominating in a given material.

ACULEATE SILKS

The fibrous protein produced by different insect species as silk is most varied in primary and in secondary structure. Apart from the classical extended, parallel-β fibroin types, we have found conformations corresponding to cross-β types, α-helical types and even the collagen type (Rudall, 1962). The silks of Hymenopteran aculeate larvae (bees, wasps, ants) are all of the α-helical type. The X-ray diffraction patterns of these are more informative than in the case of most other natural α-helical

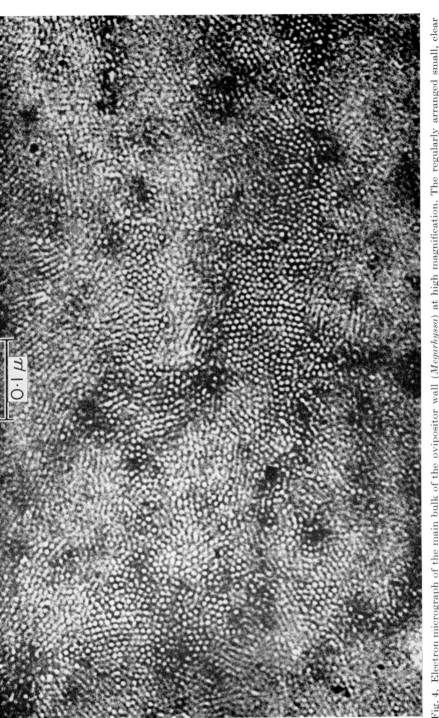

Fig. 4. Electron micrograph of the main bulk of the ovipositor wall (*Megarhyssa*) at high magnification. The regularly arranged small, clear areas are cross-sections of chitin rods separated by darkly staining areas (protein).

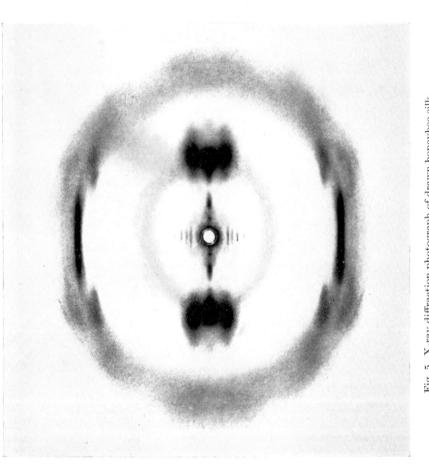

Fig. 5. X-ray diffraction photograph of drawn honeybee silk.

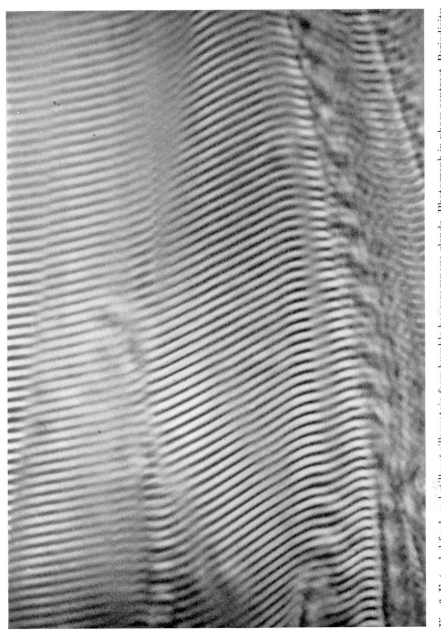

Fig. 6. Extruded fresh and still wet silk protein from bumble-bee serogenous glands. Photograph in phase contrast. Periodicity of bands just under 1·5 μ.

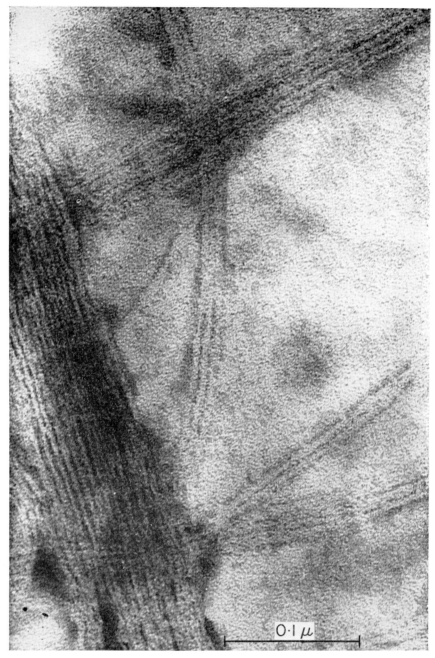

Fig. 7. Partly separated silk filaments from preparation as in Fig. 6. Electron micrograph of negatively stained specimen.

proteins. In addition there are a number of striking macromolecular interactions which are of special interest.

A sample diffraction pattern of drawn honeybee silk is shown in Fig. 5 and serves to illustrate the degree of perfection of detail that can be obtained, being comparable perhaps with some optical transforms of models of α-helices produced by Fraser & MacRae (1961) and with information obtained from byssus retractor muscle (Cohen & Holmes, 1963). Much work is required on X-ray, electron microscopy and bio-chemical fronts to develop our knowledge of this structure to a greater extent. Of the meridional series of reflections we can say this: in the relative intensity of orders the patterns differ most markedly in com-paring honeybee, bumble bee, colonial wasp and solitary wasp, a sample from the last having been illustrated previously (Rudall, 1962). Measure-ments made by E. D. Atkins of the honeybee silk shown in Fig. 5 indicate an axial period of at least 280 Å.

For some time W. R. Kenchington has been developing our knowledge of the structure and behaviour of the silk glands in various bee larvae. In the honeybee the silk is stored as microscopic tactoids in the lumen of the tubular glands. Both at the optical level and in the E.M. these tactoids are seen to be cross striated as if composed of filaments of defined length and with the filament ends all at one level across the tactoid. In bumble bees some tactoids are present attached to the anterior wall of the gland but the usual arrangement is that of well-defined laminae or rods. For example Fig. 6 is a phase contrast picture of silk allowed to flow out on to a microscope slide. The width of the regularly spaced bright bands is a little over 1 μ; in polarized light the substructure shows positive birefringence in a direction perpendicular to these bands. The bands appear in Fig. 6 like sections through layers or laminae but in reality each band is a rod, rectangular in section, and towards the bottom of Fig. 6 approximate end views of these rods are to be seen.

The polarization optics and the regularity of the bands in Fig. 6 indicate that close packed protein filaments run across the width of the bands. This is readily confirmed by electron microscopy. It recalls the structure of the A band in striated muscle and if there is as yet insufficient positive evidence that the silk filaments are joined at their middle regions they are at least closely associated with their ends at common levels and the filaments perpendicular to these levels. With material from the gland lumen, individual filaments begin to separate in dilute salt solutions (0·1 M KCl) and some negatively stained preparations by N. E. Flower of *Bombus* silk are shown in Fig. 7. On the whole the filaments appear of uniform width (about 40 Å) with some evidence that each filament consists of two rods about 20 Å in diameter. Where the filament twists the profile may measure only about 20 Å. Occasionally where a number of filaments remain adhering together there is longi-tudinal periodicity of about 170 Å; we have yet to determine whether this feature is restricted to one region of the filament length such as near its centre.

What might this arrangement signify? During the extrusion of the stored secretion the filaments, initially packed side by side, are sheared and flow past one another. There are specialized cells in the most anterior wall of the gland which may produce enzymes or other substances that facilitate the rearrangement of the filaments in the rods. It seems possible that as the filaments flow over one another new interfilament linkages can be formed which may play some significant part in the production of strong insoluble fibres.

These silks are not easy to study. The material is reasonably available only for limited periods of the year, nor is there the vast quantity of material to hand as in the study of muscle. Yet the situation is an important one in which to explore the comparative structure and behaviour of α-helical protein systems.

CALCIUM CITRATE IN AN INSECT

There is a large gland in the body wall of the seventh ventral sternite or sub-genital plate of female mantids producing characteristically shaped crystals which we have determined as calcium citrate hexahydrate (Parker & Rudall, 1955). The fully developed crystals are incorporated into the ootheca at laying and are especially abundant lining the egg cavity and exit pathway for the emerging larva. The crystals develop in size as the young adult proceeds to make the first ootheca and new generations of crystals start to grow in size after each laying. We have described elsewhere the influence of injected calcium salts on the growth of these crystals, calcium carbonate has no effect but calcium citrate considerably increases the size of the crystals (Rudall, 1964).

The first most noteworthy aspect of these crystals is the system of membranes which surround them (Fig. 8). The end face membranes are thicker and the top face of the trapeziform profile consists of fibrous structures joining the two end plates, while the two sides and the bottom wall appear uniform and thinner. As the crystals grow the membranes increase in area and always cover the crystals. However, the thickness of the top and end face membranes also appear to increase with the size of the crystals, prompting the question as to whether there is a tendency towards a stoicheiometric relation between these membranes and the enclosed citrate. The side and bottom membranes are readily dispersed by washing in water but are fixed after treatment in formalin and osmic acid. The top fibrous membranes and the end membranes persist after washing in water but the top membrane is readily digested in trypsin, while the end membranes are more resistant. Membranes surrounding cell inclusions are common enough but the unusual feature here is the distinctive character of those covering the definably different faces of

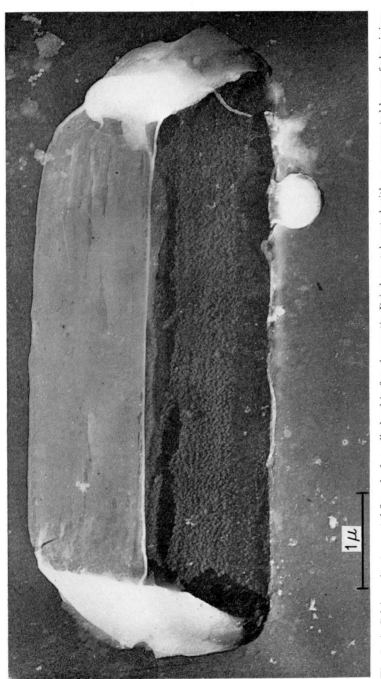

Fig. 8. A, Calcium citrate crystal from body-wall gland in female mantis. Dried crystal coated with an evaporated layer of aluminium to support the membranes, and then the citrate was washed away in water.

Fig. 8. B, Calcium citrate crystal fixed in osmic acid vapour and then the citrate was dissolved in distilled water. Collapsed membranes, shadowed with gold-palladium.

In A and B the so-called end plates are the thicker rectangular membranes to left and right of the figures. The top fibrous membrane is seen at the top in A and centrally in B while the thin 'side walls' are seen in B, bulging out at the top and bottom of the figure.

the crystals. The crystal structure of calcium citrate has not been determined owing to the difficulty of obtaining uniform crystals of sufficient size for single crystal analysis. These mantis crystals are certainly uniform and at least approaching the size where satisfactory analyses could be made; we are engaged upon such a study in order to determine which chemical groups constitute the separate faces of the crystals.

As to the nature of the membranes, we can ask if some are the site of synthesis of citrate and its controlled deposition as calcium citrate. Or the membranes may be partly composed of organic constituents necessary to the proper functioning of the ootheca structure or perhaps they play some part in the successful emergence of the larvae. Surgically it is quite easy to remove the calcium citrate gland and oothecae are produced. It remains to be seen whether the structure of the egg chambers and passages are normal and whether the developing larvae survive and emerge.

Our original description of calcium citrate crystals was of those taken from the body wall gland, though we could also see identical crystals in the layed ootheca (Parker & Rudall, 1955). Hackman & Goldberg (1960) made an analysis of the oothecae of *Orthodera ministralis* (Fab.) and were not able to find any citrate. The young praying mantids had emerged and the oothecae were cut in half, presumably lengthwise, and washed. If we assume that the washing was the same as that described for cockroach oothecae then this would entail soaking overnight in water containing a small amount of synthetic detergent followed by 'rubbing and repeated washing, washed thoroughly in distilled water and finally air dried'. We are not able to repeat the exact washing procedure used by Hackman and Goldberg. However we can state that the calcium citrate crystals taken from the gland and air dried on a slide, dissolve completely in excess distilled water overnight leaving the ghosts shown in Fig. 8. We would consider that the discrepancy between their results and ours could be explained by the loss of calcium citrate during their washing procedure. Although Hackman and Goldberg appear to find no citrate in oothecae where the larvae had emerged, it is unlikely that the citrate has been lost during development and hatching.

It is unlikely that the mantis *O. ministralis* is an exception and does not possess a 'calcium citrate gland'. Dr. Hackman kindly provided us with oothecae of the species he studied. Numerous crystals of the typical calcium citrate form were observable in the oothecal wall. Unhatched oothecae, which he also provided, produced young insects but unfortunately none survived to maturity. In the case of the New Zealand mantis, which Tillyard (1926) regards as *O. ministralis* introduced into that country from Australia, we succeeded in rearing adults. The calcium citrate gland is present in typical form and crystals taken from it are just the same in form and in the presence of surface membranes as in the other mantids we had studied. An X-ray powder diagram of these gland crystals of *O. ministralis* (N.Z. species) is shown in Fig. 9A and is compared with synthetic calcium citrate hexahydrate, Fig. 9B. There is identity of structure as was observed originally for other mantid species by comparison of crystal structures and of infrared absorption spectra with laboratory preparations of calcium citrate (Parker & Rudall, 1955).

DISCUSSION

Three structures found in insects have been considered because of the new information they are providing at the molecular level. While chemical studies on exo- and endo-cuticle are difficult, because of the drastic procedures necessary to dissolve them, physical studies of the intact solid state using X-ray analysis, electron microscopy and infrared absorption are an important guide in defining the problems of structure. At its simplest the X-ray studies tell us that the chitin chains are in small groups rather than large ones and that these groups are separated by protein, the tanning of which stabilizes the complex. But there are a number of well-defined dimensions which we believe are best interpreted as a close geometrical fitting of protein on chitin.

We have dealt with just one of the chitin/protein systems, that which shows an ordered macromolecular system repeating every 31 Å along the length of the chitin chains. Apparently there is an accurate design of chitin plus protein at the molecular level, this design and its variations being regarded as important in the detailed functioning of the cuticle. Our current electron microscope studies of Hymenopteran cuticle demonstrate beautiful regularity of structure at the molecular level. It also impresses us with the many problems remaining to be solved before we can say we understand the molecular structure and biochemistry of cuticle.

The silks have been included in this review entitled 'Skeletal Structures'. They have in general an extramural function, protecting the eggs, supporting eggs or surrounding the larva and pupa. Like the chitin/ protein system of the cuticle they persist as a solid well-designed extra-cellular deposition but, unlike the cuticle, they must be regarded as 'dead'. Silks are one of the very instructive products of insects. Our first confidence in the long chain structure of proteins rests on Meyer and Marks's X-ray studies of silk fibroin. Since then silks have demonstrated the existence of transformable cross-β proteins in *Chrysopa* egg stalks, of collagen conformation without hydroxyproline in gooseberry sawfly larval silk, and new types of α-helical protein in mantis ootheca and in the aculeate silks described here. While it has been customary to visualize the silk stored in the lumen of serogenous glands as an ill-defined viscous mass of protein molecules, our studies of mantis oothecal protein, and particularly those on the aculeate silks, show that there are elaborate stages of organization between the act of secretion and the fabrication of a membranous ootheca or silken fibre.

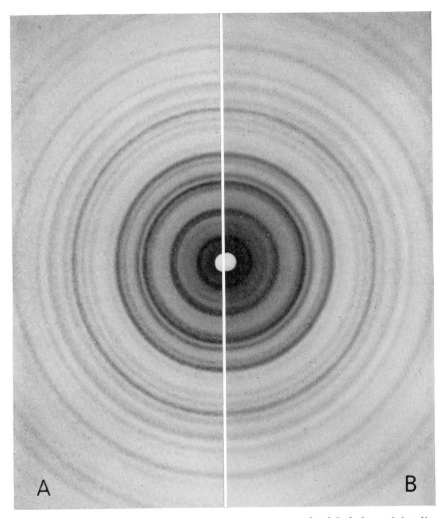

Fig. 9. A, X-ray powder photograph of calcium citrate crystals of *Orthodera ministralis* (New Zealand species). Crystals larger.
  B, Calcium citrate hexahydrate as prepared in the laboratory. Crystals smaller.

We have also dealt with the specialized crystals of calcium citrate which take part in the formation of mantis oothecae. They have, perhaps, a wider connection with problems of skeletal structures in that calcium citrate is a constituent of the mineral phase of vertebrate bone and teeth. The membranes surrounding the crystals of calcium citrate have attracted our attention and one of their functions may be to determine the size and shape of the crystals so that they can be conveniently excreted through a narrow duct to the exterior. A possible relation was seen with the control of the size and shape of apatite crystals in tooth enamel (Rudall, 1964) and recent electron microscope studies of growing teeth do indeed find some special membrane structures surrounding the apatite crystals there (Travis & Glimcher, 1964).

This work was supported by a U.S. Public Health Grant, GM 07399.

REFERENCES

Andersen, S. O. & Weis-Fogh, T. (1964). *Adv. Insect Physiol.* **2**, 1.
Cohen, C. & Holmes, K. C. (1963). *J. molec. Biol.* **6**, 423.
Evans, A. C. (1938). *Proc. R. ent. Soc. Lond.* A **13**, 107.
Fraser, R. D. B. & MacRae, T. P. (1961). *J. molec. Biol.* **3**, 640.
Hackman, R. H. & Goldberg, M. (1960). *J. Insect Physiol.* **5**, 73.
Parker, K. D. & Rudall, K. M. (1955). *Biochim. biophys. Acta* **17**, 287.
Picken, L. E. R. & Lotmar, W. (1950). *Nature, Lond.* **165**, 599.
Rudall, K. M. (1962). In *Comparative Biochemistry*, Vol. 4, p. 397, Ed. M. Florkin and H. S. Mason. New York: Academic Press.
Rudall, K. M. (1963). *Adv. Insect Physiol.* **1**, 257.
Rudall, K. M. (1964). In *Proceedings of an International Symposium on the Composition, Properties and Fundamental Structure of Enamel*, p. 132, Ed. Slack and Fearnhead. Bristol: Wright.
Tillyard, R. J. (1926). *The Insects of Australia and New Zealand.* Sydney: Angus and Robertson.
Travis, D. F. & Glimcher, M. J. (1964). *J. Cell Biol.* **23**, 447.

DISCUSSION

V. B. Wigglesworth: In the production of silk by the silkworm the soluble fibroinogen of the silk gland is said to be subjected to shearing forces in the spinneret which serve to unfold the long-chain molecules and to eliminate the hydration shells that separate them, so that they 'crystallize' in an insoluble form. Do similar processes occur in these other silks?

K. M. Rudall: Sir Vincent Wigglesworth reminded us that a shearing of the protein in the case of *Bombyx mori* silk leads to its insolubility (see Ramsden, W. (1938) *Nature, Lond.* **142**, 1120). Other contributions on the subject are reviewed by C. H. Bamford, A. Elliott & W. W. Hanby (*Synthetic Polypeptides*, New York: Academic Press, 1956). There is no precisely described structure available for the silk within the glands of silkworms that would enable us to say that filaments lie accurately side by side within the gland and that, on spinning, they slide over one another,

changes which we *are* able to describe for bee larval silk. In Ramsden's
experiments, where he pressed soluble gland silk between glass or mica
plates and observed a very marked decrease in solubility, we do not know
to what extent he has unfolded or denatured proteins by extending them.
The problems are somewhat like those which existed in the muscle field
where contraction could be looked upon as due either to chain folding or
to sliding of filaments past one another. A similar dilemma is with us in
the spinning of silk : is there some chain unfolding or is sliding of filaments
past one another more important ? In the muscle field all the evidence is
in favour of the sliding model and against a folding of chains sufficiently
extensive to account for the dimensional changes during contraction,
but it does not exclude changes in the conformation of molecules that
would be associated with localized chemical reactions. In the case of the
various silk-spinning phenomena it may emerge that a very significant
event is the sliding of filaments and that there may or may not be some
conformational changes in molecules which could be of importance in the
process of insolubilization of the protein.

AUTHOR INDEX

Numbers in italics refer to pages in the References at the end of each article.

A

Aerts, F. E., 55, 56, 63, *72, 76*
Agarwal, H. C., 31, *35*
Alexander, P., 65, *72*
Allen, T. H., 63, *73*
Ammon, H., 60, *75*
Andersen, B., 1, 4, *12*
Andersen, S. O., 51, 52, 59, *72*, 84, *91*

B

Baldwin, E., 33, *35*
Bailey, K., 51, *73*
Bamford, C. H., 91, *91*
Barbier, M., 31, *36*
Barthmeyer, H., 55, *76*
Barton, D. H. R., 65, *72*
Bauer, S., 40, *47*
Beament, J. W. L., 2, 3, *12*
Beard, R. L., 34, *35, 72, 73*
Beck, S. D., 31, *35*
Becker, E., 66, 69, *73, 75*
Beckmann, R., 67, *73*
Beenakkers, A. M. Th., 18, 22, *27*
Bellamy, D., 71, *73*
Bergh, S. G. van der, 33, *35, 37*
Bergmann, E. D., 32, *35*
Berridge, M. J., 6, *12*
Biekert, E., 64, 67, 69, 70, *73*
Bishai, F. R., 15, 16, 17, *27, 28*
Blaschko, H., 65, *73*
Bode, Chr., 16, *28*
Bodine, J. H., 63, *73*
Boné, G., 6, *12*
Bowers, W. S., 43, *47*
Boyland, E., 71, *73*
Boyle, P. J., 4, *12*
Brandau, H., 16, *28*
Bricteux-Grégoire, S., 50, *73*
Bridges, P. M., 33, *37*
Bridges, R. G., 30
Bronsert, U., 23, *27*
Brooks, M. A., 50, *73, 76*
Brosemer, R. W., 16, 18, 20, 22, *27*
Brown, B. R., 65, *73*
Brown, C. H., 54, 55, *73*
Brunet, P. C. J., 50, 55, 58, 60, 62, 63, 64, *73, 75, 76*

B (continued)

Bückmann, D., 70, *73, 75*
Bücher, Th., 15, 16, 17, 18, 20, 22, 23, *27, 28*
Bullock, M. W., *81*
Burdette, W. C., *81*
Bursell, E., 33, *35*
Butenandt, A., 31, *35*, 64, 66, 67, 68, 69, 70, *73, 81*
Buys, K. S., 39, *47*

C

Cabib, E., 42, *47*
Caldwell, P. C., 5, *12*
Campbell, F. L., 52, *73*
Candy, D. J., 32, *36*, 42, 44, *47*
Casida, J. E., 31, *35*
Caspari, E., 66, 70, *73*
Chadwick, L. E., 33, *36*
Chen, P. S., 49, 50, *74, 75*
Chevais, S., 66, *74*
Chino, H., 32, *36*, 41, *74*
Claudatus, J., 71, *74*
Clayton, R. B., 31, *36*
Clegg, J. S., 32, *36*, 42, *47*
Clements, A. N., 35, *36*, 40, 46, *47*, 81
Clemons, R. D., 10, *12*
Cohen, C., 87, *91*
Colhoun, E. H., 65, 72, *73, 74*
Conway, E. J., 4, *12*
Copeland, E., 8, *12*
Corrigan, J. J., 33, *36*
Cottrell, C. B., 59, 63, *74*
Craig, R., 6, *12*
Cromartie, R. J. T., 67, *73*
Crone, H. D., 30, *36*

D

Dalgliesh, C. E., 31, *36*, 49, 59, 66, *74, 75*
Danneel, R., 67, *74*
Davey, K. G., 34, *36*, 65, 72, *74*
Davies, J. B., 65, *74*
Decleir, R., 55, 56, *72, 76*
Delbrück, A., 16, 17, *28*
Dennell, R., 50, 54, 56, 57, 59, *74*
Derjugin, W. von, 67, *73*
Desai, R. M., 45, *47*
Dethier, V. G., 32, *36*

SUBJECT INDEX

A

A-bands, of flight muscle, 26
Acetate,
  incorporation into fat, 40, 41, 47
  incorporation into sterols, 31
Acetyl-CoA-transacetylase, 60
Acetylcholine, 34
Active transport, 1–12
  of chloride ions, 11
  of inorganic ions, 4–11
  of potassium ions, 4, 6, 9
  of sodium ions, 2, 7, 9
  of water, 1–4, 11
Adenine, 46
Adrenaline, 34
Aedes,
  uptake and transfer of inorganic ions
    by, 6, 7, 8, 9, 11
Aeschna,
  chloride ion transport in, 11
Alanine, 33, 37
  accumulation during anoxia, 32
Albumin,
  in haemolymph, 45
Allantoin, 46
Allantoicase, 46
Allantoinase, 46
Amine oxidase, 65
Amino acid oxidases, 45
Amino acids,
  as energy sources, 33, 37
  metabolism in fat body of, 45
γ-Aminobutyric acid, 34
Aminocarboxylic acids,
  from hydrolysis of resilin, 51
Amino-phenol
  as degradation product of sclerotin,
    54
Aminoquinones,
  involvement in tanning, 53
Ammonia, 33, 47
Anlage (precursor muscle), 16
Anthoxanthins, 65
Anthranilic acid, 68, 71, 72
Anthranilylglycine, 72
Anthraquinones, 65
Anticholinesterases,
  effect on sodium ion transport of, 9, 11

Ants,
  pheromone produced by, 35
  structure of silk of, 86
Aphids,
  pigments of, 65
Aphrodite,
  chitin/protein system of, 84
Apis,
  sterol metabolism in, 31
Arginase, 45
Argotis,
  aromatic amino acid synthesis in, 50
Aromatic amino acids,
  metabolism, 50, 51, 59–62, 65, 66
  requirements and intake of, 49, 50
Arthropods,
  chromogens of, 55
  ommochromes of, 69
Ascorbate, 46
Aspartate,
  transamination in housefly, 33
ATP, 5, 32, 33, 42
  in fat metabolism, 40, 41
  in protein synthesis, 45

B

Bees,
  development of muscle of, 17, 23
  structure of fat body of, 39
  structure of silk of, 86, 87, 92
  trehalose concentration in haemo-
    lymph of, 42
Beetles,
  dihydroxyphenolic compounds in, 55
  quinonoid compounds in, 65
  requirement for carnitine of, 30
Benzoic acid, 62
Benzoquinone, 65
Benzoylglucoside, 64
Blatta,
  quinone tanning in, 55, 57
  phenolic glucosides in, 64
Blattella,
  aromatic amino acid metabolism of,
    49, 50
  sterol metabolism in, 32
Blood proteins, 45